Michael Faraday

Man of Simplicity

By the same author

*

HUMPHRY DAVY

Faraday's Statue at the Royal Institution
(*Courtesy of the Institution of Electrical Engineers*)

Michael Faraday
Man of Simplicity

by
JAMES KENDALL
M.A., D.Sc., LL.D., F.R.S.

*Professor of Chemistry in the University
of Edinburgh; Past President of the
Royal Society of Edinburgh*

FABER AND FABER
24 Russell Square
London

First published in mcmlv
by Faber and Faber Limited
24 Russell Square London W.C.1
Printed in Great Britain by
Latimer Trend & Co Ltd Plymouth

To my sister
Elizabeth
with grateful affection

*

*We too have simple childhood memories
And now, once more together, can recall
Events that loomed so large when we were small,
Still not to us mere trivialities.*

Contents

9

Illustrations

11

Introduction

Oh, Mr. Faraday, simple Mr. Faraday!
  Did you of enlightenment consider this an age?
Bless your simplicity, deep in electricity,
  But, in social matters, unsophisticated sage!
Punch (1853)

It has always pleased the public to regard great scientists, outside their own special fields of investigation, as artless children, learned men in the laboratory but innocents abroad. Tales are told about almost every scientific genius to illustrate his inability to cope with plain practical difficulties. Take, for instance, the story of Isaac Newton and his pet cat. A hole was made in the door of Newton's study to enable this animal to leave the room without distracting him during his calculations. When the cat had a kitten, Newton pondered the problem thoroughly and then called in a carpenter to cut a second hole in the door for the kitten's convenience.

To the early Victorians, Michael Faraday was at the same time a miracle man and a source of mild amusement. Everyone recognized that upon him had fallen the mantle of his master Humphry Davy, and that he was undoubtedly the greatest scientist of his age. All Britain was proud of his achievements, but the hard-headed business magnates and politicians of that period were never able to understand how a person with such a brain could be, from their point of view, so 'simple'. Why did he refuse to turn his intellect to industrial

13

Introduction

topics, to assist them in consolidating British trade supremacy and Britain's international prestige, to speed up prosperity and to make his own fortune as well? Why, in particular, did he in the era of steam fritter his energies away, year after year, on a mere toy like electricity?

One question they asked him repeatedly, when they visited the Royal Institution and saw him perform some experiment: 'But what's the use of it?' Faraday usually made the same answer that Benjamin Franklin made under similar circumstances: 'What's the use of a baby? Some day it will grow up!' On one occasion, however, he replied differently. Mr. Gladstone, then Chancellor of the Exchequer, had interrupted him in a description of his work on electricity to put the impatient inquiry: 'But, after all, what use is it?' Like a flash of lightning came the response: 'Why, sir, there is every probability that you will soon be able to tax it!'

How wise this simple Mr. Faraday was! We who live in an age that is dependent upon electricity for so many essentials— transport, communications, light, heat and power—can appreciate now the practical outcome of Faraday's purely theoretical researches. We are not entitled, however, to feel complacent and superior over our sagacity after the event. It is just as fashionable to snicker at Einstein to-day as it was for Newton's contemporaries to snicker at Newton. And if we do not joke about atomic energy, which will supersede electricity as surely as electricity superseded steam, it is only because we know enough about atomic energy already to know that it is no joking matter.

Careful analysis of Faraday's character discloses that he was indeed simple in the sense of being single-minded, natural, unaffected, unpretentious. Here he differed from his predecessor, Humphry Davy, who possessed a most complex

Introduction

temperament. Davy was not only a scientist, he was poet, novelist, essayist, angler, traveller and man of the world; Faraday had no ambition except to advance human knowledge. Davy enjoyed being a society idol, President of the Royal Society of London and a baronet; Faraday secluded himself from society and refused such honours. It is almost fantastic to note that when Davy was a boy of twenty, working at the Pneumatic Institution at Bristol on laughing gas, he wrote a novel *Imla, the Man of Simplicity*, of which he thought he himself was the hero. If ever there was a man of absolute simplicity, it was Michael Faraday.

Both original and secondary sources for the framework of Faraday's life and work are abundant. First in importance is the two-volume *Life and Letters of Faraday*, by Dr. Bence Jones, Secretary of the Royal Institution (1870). Two shorter books written by his intimate colleagues are also of great value—*Faraday as a Discoverer*, by John Tyndall (1868), and *Michael Faraday*, by J. H. Gladstone (1872). More recent biographies that merit special mention are *Michael Faraday: His Life and Work*, by Silvanus P. Thompson (1901), and *A Tribute to Michael Faraday*, by Rollo Appleyard (1931).

Faraday's life is so closely linked with that of Sir Humphry Davy at three stages—the start of his scientific career, the continental journey, and the misunderstandings that arose between the two men later—that it has proved impossible for me to avoid a certain amount of duplication here with my previous book *Humphry Davy: 'Pilot' of Penzance*. Such duplication has been minimized as far as possible by making Faraday the central figure of the various episodes instead of Davy, but since the only direct evidence on many vital matters originates from Faraday (Davy remaining silent) I am forced to repeat a number of essential letters and quotations. Space considerations preclude me from defending

Introduction

Davy's conduct in detail, but I believe I have done him full justice in the volume cited above.

Faraday's *Experimental Researches in Electricity, Chemistry and Physics*, published in various scientific journals, were collected into four large volumes during his lifetime (1839–1859), and a complete record of his laboratory notes, carefully transcribed from day to day during the years 1820–1862, was issued under the editorial supervision of Thomas Martin in seven still larger volumes, entitled *Faraday's Diary*, between 1932 and 1936. It will be obvious that the present book cannot pretend to offer a comprehensive account of these purely scientific investigations; they are discussed, in fact, only in bare outline. My primary purpose, as in *Humphry Davy: 'Pilot' of Penzance*, is to unfold in simple narrative form the life story of a true genius; scientific achievements, while by no means neglected, are described for the layman rather than for the expert, and serve in the main as a background for a study of character.

As a man Michael Faraday inspires such deep affection, as a scientist he excites such intense admiration, that I have found it very difficult to express my feelings in adequate words. I can only trust that I shall be successful in winning the hearts of my readers, especially my younger readers, for whom this book is specifically written, to sympathize with my sentiments. *Sancta simplicitas* is indeed the keynote to a proper understanding of Michael Faraday, unsophisticated sage, nature's gentleman.

I wish to express my gratitude to the proprietors of *Punch* for permission to incorporate in this volume several quotations from that periodical between 1853 and 1867. Also to Thomas Nelson and Sons, Ltd., of Edinburgh, for consenting to allow me to repeat matter included in my earlier book: *Great Discoveries by Young Chemists* (1953). This repetition

Introduction

mainly consists of extracts from original sources which are indispensable to any biography of Faraday, but in a few cases my own comments upon certain critical points have been unavoidably duplicated.

In addition, I have again to accord my sincere thanks to my nieces, Marion Waters and Elizabeth Williams, for the material help they have given me in collating references and in correcting proof. Also to my secretary, Miss I. E. Inch, for typing my manuscript.

I hope that none of my readers will consider that I have been too familiar in my general employment of proper names. I am quite prepared to admit that this is not in accordance with the custom of the age in which Michael lived; no doubt Sarah followed nineteenth-century habit by invariably addressing her husband as 'Mr. Faraday' in the presence of company, perhaps even in connubial solitude. But formality towards Faraday is just as irksome to me as formality towards Davy, except in my brief (and, I trust, reverent) discussion of his religious beliefs. At any rate, I have never been so presumptuous as to call him Mike. I do not know how my own students refer to me behind my back, but I should be very vexed if they always called me Professor Kendall.

JAMES KENDALL

Edinburgh
May 1954

CHAPTER ONE

A Boy is Bewitched

I love a smith's shop and anything related to smithery.
My father was a smith.

MICHAEL FARADAY (1841)

It is 9th April 1812, and the great Humphry Davy is giving the last of a series of four lectures at the Royal Institution. He has been the rage of London since he, a mere youth of twenty-two, delivered his maiden address there eleven years ago: 'literary and scientific, practical and theoretical, blue-stockings and women of fashion, old and young, all crowded —eagerly crowded—the lecture-room.' To-day, however, is a very special occasion, and it is probable that the minds of Davy and of most of his audience are not concentrated entirely on the subject of his discourse, *Metals*; this despite the fact that some of the metals exhibited—such as potassium, a piece of which he throws into a bowl of water, where it swims on the surface and releases hydrogen to burn with a beautiful lilac glow—were discovered by Davy himself. For only the previous day the renowned investigator had received the accolade of knighthood from the Prince Regent; the former apothecary's apprentice is henceforth Sir Humphry Davy. Furthermore, although it has not yet been officially announced, he knows and many suspect that this is, in all likelihood, his farewell lecture; he plans to relinquish his official duties at the Royal Institution and proposes to devote

18

FOUR LECTURES

being part of a Course on

The Elements of

CHEMICAL PHILOSOPHY

Delivered by

SIR H. DAVY

LLD. Sec.RS. FRSE. MRIA. MRI. &c.

AT THE

Royal Institution

And taken off from Notes

BY

M. FARADAY

1812

The famous 'Quarto Volume' and its Title-page

himself entirely, in future, to original research there. This latter intention he may find a little difficult to fulfil, since a third distracting influence (perhaps the most powerful of all) still remains to be mentioned. He is due to be married, only two days from now, and many of the ladies in the lecture-theatre who have sighed vainly for a tender glance from his bright eyes will be brooding more about the wealthy widow who is to wed him than about the chemistry to which they feigned devotion for his dear sake. There are indeed many reasons why the first scientist of his age should prove incapable of casting his wonted spell over his listeners.

While the attention of others is wandering, however, one young man is absolutely enthralled, utterly bewitched, from start to finish. He is sitting in the centre of the gallery, just over the clock opposite the lecturer. He hangs upon every word that is uttered, he watches every gesture that is made and every detail of the experiments that are performed, yet somehow or other he manages to jot down rough notes and to draw crude diagrams of all the apparatus employed in the experiments. These notes and drawings, as soon as he can find time for the task, are amplified from his memory, are reproduced in copper-plate manuscript with care, and are bound by his own hands into a quarto volume. This volume, covering the complete series of four lectures and extending to no fewer than 386 pages, provides him with a permanent record of his rapture. Let us peep over his shoulder and read just one brief extract from the final lecture, which will suffice to indicate the enchantment Davy has already cast upon him.

'Having thus given the general character of the metals, Sir H. Davy proceeded to make a few observations on the connection of science with the other parts of life. Here it would be improper for me to follow him. I should merely injure and destroy the beautiful, the sublime observations that fell from his lips. He spoke in the most energetic and luminous manner of the advancement of the arts and sciences, of the connection that had always existed between them and other parts of a nation's economy. He noticed the peculiar congeries of great men in all departments of life that generally appeared together, but, by an unaccountable omission, forgot himself, though I venture to say no one else present did.'

And now let us assume that we are also present at Davy's last lecture and are able to foresee the future. We shall be gazing at this 'chiel amang us taking notes' with the same reverence and admiration he displays for Davy, since he is destined to serve the Royal Institution himself during more than fifty years, to thrill thousands with his own eloquence as a lecturer, and to make discoveries in science as important as those of his illustrious predecessor. His name is Michael Faraday.

Faraday was of humble origin and was never ashamed to admit it, as the heading to this chapter shows. The first member of his family of whom we have any knowledge, Richard ffaraday, was a stonemason and tiler; the parish register of the village of Clapham, in the north-west corner of Yorkshire, contains the names of ten of his children, born between 1708 and 1730. Richard is also described in this register as a 'separatist', and later members of the family all belonged to the little religious body known as Sandemanians. Michael's life-long adherence to the tenets of this sect will be discussed in a subsequent chapter.

It is uncertain whether Robert Faraday, Michael's grandfather, born in 1724, was a son or a nephew of the aforesaid Richard. He made a good marriage, since his wife, Elizabeth Dean, owned a small estate called Clapham Wood Hall, but he also had ten children, and financial stringency compelled his sons to take up manual occupations. Michael's father, James, born in 1761, became a blacksmith. In an attempt to bolster up the family resources, an old stone barn near the Hall was converted into a cotton mill, but this had to be sold in 1790, and ten years later the nine surviving children disposed of Clapham Wood Hall itself for the meagre sum of £380. Long before this happened, however, James had left his village smithy and migrated to London.

James had married, in 1786, Margaret Hastwell, a farmer's daughter of Mallerstang, near Kirkby Stephen in Westmorland. He is reported to have walked prodigious distances across the fells—Clapham itself lies deep in the Pennines at the foot of Ingleborough—to visit her during his courting days, and we shall find that Michael inherited his pedestrian ability. Soon after their marriage, the young couple left the Yorkshire Moors to try their fortunes in the far-away metropolis, and it was at Newington Butts, near Walworth on the Surrey side of the Thames, that their third child Michael was born on 22nd September 1791.

Things continued to go badly, however, and in 1796 James moved his wife and children across the river to some rooms over a coachhouse in Jacob's Well Mews, near Manchester Square. His health was slowly deteriorating; he finally gave up his own smithy and worked as a journeyman. In a pathetic letter to his brother Thomas at Clapham he wrote: 'I am seldom off work for a whole day together, yet I am under the necessity (through pain) of being from work part of almost every day.' Shortly after making another removal to Weymouth Street, near Portland Place, he died in October 1810.

In such circumstances, it will be obvious that Michael's childhood was one of extreme poverty. He himself states:

A Boy is Bewitched

'My education was of the most ordinary description, consisting of little more than the rudiments of reading, writing and arithmetic at a common day-school. My hours out of school were passed at home and in the streets.' He used to point out to friends later where he played at marbles in Spanish Place, near Jacob's Well Mews, and where he took care of his younger sister Margaret in Manchester Square.

The following tale of his schooldays is related by one of his nephews. When very young, Michael was taken to a dame's school by his elder brother Robert. His inability to pronounce the letter 'r' properly was seized upon as an excuse by the harsh schoolmistress to send 'Wobert' out with a halfpenny to buy a cane, so that the little culprit could be properly flogged. Robert, however, seething with rage, threw the halfpenny over a wall and ran home to inform his mother, who straightway went into action herself and removed both boys from the school.

Arising from this story, the intriguing question has often been asked: 'How did Michael get his unusual name, a name which occurs nowhere else in the family records?'[1] Michael himself, when questioned on this point after he had become famous, used to assert there was an Irish strain in his ancestry, and proved his assertion by reciting extracts from his lectures in a perfect Irish brogue. Now it is probable that all this was pure leg-pull, since our austere hero simply revelled in jokes of such nature. On the other hand, it is quite possible that there may have been Irish blood on his mother's side, blood

---

[1] Dr. James Riley (*The Hammer and the Anvil*, 1954) has since delved into the history of the Hastwells of Kirkby Stephen, and has noted that Michael was named after his maternal grandfather. A double link existed between the Faraday and Hastwell families, both Sandemanians, since Robert, the eldest brother of James, married Mary, an elder sister of Margaret, in 1777. They also named one of their five sons Michael.

which rose to boiling-point at once in defence of her offspring in the incident described above. Both Robert and Michael himself were very quick-tempered when provoked, as will appear in due course. Finally, just look at the plate facing page 152, which depicts Michael holding the bar of heavy glass with which he first demonstrated the effect of magnetism on light. Does it not bring to mind the phrase: 'With my shillelagh in my hand?'

At the age of thirteen, Michael's schooling ended, and he was taken on trial for a year as errand-boy by Mr. George Riebau, a bookseller in Blandford Street. He has been portrayed as sliding along the London pavements 'with a load of brown curls upon his head and a packet of newspapers under his arm'. He himself relates: 'It was my duty, when I first went, to carry round the papers that were lent out by my master. Often on a Sunday morning I got up very early and took them round. Then I had to call for them again, and frequently, when I was told "The paper is not done with; you must call back," I would beg to be allowed to have it; for my next place might be a mile off, and then I should have to return over the ground again, losing much time and being very unhappy if I was unable to get home to make myself neat, and to go with my parents to their place of worship.'

Never did he forget this, his earliest occupation. One of his nieces states that he rarely passed a newspaper boy in the street without making some kind remark. Another recalls him saying to her: 'I always feel a tenderness for those boys, because I once carried newspapers myself.'

The young errand-boy was not immune, however, from boyish pranks and misadventures. A near relative tells how, in later life, Michael visited the shop where his father had formerly worked as a blacksmith, and asked to be permitted to look over the place. On arriving at a part of the premises

A Boy is Bewitched

where there was an opening in the floor, he stopped and said: 'I very nearly lost my life there once. I was playing at pitching halfpence into a pint pot close by this hole. Having succeeded at a short distance, I stepped back to try my fortune further off, forgetting the aperture. Down I fell. If it had not happened that my father was working over an anvil fixed just below, I should have fallen on it, broken my back, and probably killed myself. As it was, my father's back just saved mine.'

On 7th October 1805, his year of trial being regarded as satisfactory, Michael was formally apprenticed for seven years to Mr. Riebau 'to learn the arts of bookbinder, stationer and bookseller', and the indentures continue: 'In consideration of his faithful service, no premium is required.' He lived over the shop; an enamelled tablet now records his connection with the place. Tyndall, his associate and subsequently his successor at the Royal Institution, relates the following story, typical of Faraday's simplicity and freedom from false pride. 'Mr. Faraday and myself quitted the Institution one evening together. He took my arm at the door and, pressing it to his side in his warm genial way, said: "Come, Tyndall, I will now show you something that will interest you." We reached Blandford Street; he paused before a stationer's shop, and then went in. On entering the shop, his usual animation seemed doubled; he looked rapidly at everything it contained. To the left was a door, through which he looked down into a little room with a window facing in front Blandford Street. Drawing me towards him, he said eagerly: "Look there, Tyndall, that was my working-place. I bound books in that little nook." '

Not only did he bind books there, when he had time to spare he read such as interested him. He himself states:

'It was in those books, in the hours after work, that I found the beginning of my philosophy. There were two that especially helped me, the *Encyclopaedia Britannica*, from which I gained my first notions of electricity, and Mrs. Marcet's *Conversations on Chemistry*, which gave me my foundation in that science. Do not suppose that I was a very deep thinker, or was marked as a precocious person. I was a very lively, imaginative person, and could believe in the *Arabian Nights* as easily as in the *Encyclopaedia*; but facts were important to me, and saved me. I could trust a fact, and always cross-examined an assertion. So when I questioned Mrs. Marcet's book by such little experiments as I could find means to perform, and found it true to the facts as I could understand them, I felt that I had got hold of an anchor in chemical knowledge, and clung fast to it. Thence my deep veneration for Mrs. Marcet: first, as one who had conferred great personal good and pleasure on me, and then as one able to convey the truth and principle of those boundless fields of knowledge which concern natural things, to the young, untaught, and inquiring mind. You may imagine my delight when I came to know Mrs. Marcet personally; how often I cast my thoughts backwards, delighting to connect the past and the present; how often, when sending a paper to her as a thank-offering, I thought of my first instructress, and such like thoughts will remain with me.'

Besides making such simple experiments in chemistry as could be defrayed in their expense by a few pence per week, Michael also constructed an electrical machine, 'first with a glass phial, afterwards with a real cylinder, as well as other electrical apparatus of a corresponding kind.' His master, Mr. Riebau, must have been an understanding man, for he encouraged him in his studies. Walking one day in Fleet Street, Michael had seen some posters in the shop windows announcing lectures on natural philosophy to be delivered by Mr.

A Boy is Bewitched

Tatum at his house in Dorset Street. With Mr. Riebau's permission (the hour was eight in the evening) Michael attended about a dozen of these lectures in the period between February 1810 and September 1811. It will be noted that these months cover the time of his father's final illness and death, and Michael was indebted to his brother Robert (now also a blacksmith and the breadwinner of the family) for the shilling he had to pay to attend each lecture. His mother was taking in lodgers at the house in Weymouth Street to make both ends meet, and Michael longed for the expiry of his apprenticeship to be able to assist her.

Meanwhile, these lectures were intensifying his interest in science and luring him towards a scientific career. He made copious and neat notes of everything that he heard; these notebooks, bound by himself, are still preserved. He learned perspective drawing, so that he might illustrate his notes with diagrams. His teacher was a French artist, Masquerier, who had once painted Napoleon's portrait but was now a refugee in London, living in a room above Riebau's shop. In return for this instruction, Michael used to dust Masquerier's room and black his boots. Forty years later Faraday went to see Masquerier at Brighton, and one who was also present, Crabb Robinson, noted in his diary: 'When Faraday was young, poor, and altogether unknown, Masquerier was kind to him; and now that he is a great man he does not forget his old friend.'

At Mr. Tatum's lectures, also, Michael met several congenial comrades of his own age. Three may be mentioned in particular—Huxtable, a medical student; Abbott, a clerk in the City; and Phillips, a chemist, later President of the Chemical Society. All three remained lifelong friends, but there can be no doubt that Benjamin Abbott came first in his affections. Abbott was a Quaker, eighteen months younger

27

A Boy is Bewitched

than Michael but with a much better education, and Michael's respect for his superior knowledge is very evident in their lengthy correspondence, extracts from which, 'possessing an interest almost beyond any other letters Faraday afterwards wrote,' will come up for citation in due course.

And in the final months of his apprenticeship Michael made yet another friend, Mr. Dance, who was a frequent customer at Riebau's bookshop. As a member of the Royal Institution, Mr. Dance gave the boy whose industry and intelligence had aroused his kindly interest tickets to four of Humphry Davy's lectures there. How stimulated Michael was by those lectures we have already seen; how the emotion they evoked in him changed the whole design of his life will appear in the next chapter.

CHAPTER TWO

Entry into the Service of Science

I am working at my old trade, the which I wish to leave at the first convenient opportunity. With respect to the progress of the sciences I know but little, and am now likely to know still less. Indeed, as long as I stop in my present situation I must resign philosophy entirely to those who are more fortunate in the possession of time and means.

Letter from Michael Faraday to
T. Huxtable (October 1812)

It is Christmas Eve, 1812, and Sir Humphry Davy is writing a letter in his study at the Royal Institution. He writes with considerable difficulty, because he is suffering from the effects of a serious explosion which occurred in the course of some experiments he was making on nitrogen trichloride a few weeks previously, and it is still uncertain whether he will retain the sight of one eye. But he wishes to send this letter off before he leaves London for further medical treatment; perhaps his uncanny intuition senses its importance.

That morning he had met a friend, Mr. Pepys of the Poultry, one of the original managers of the Royal Institution, and had shown him a communication he had just received. 'Pepys, what am I to do?' he asked. 'Here is a letter from a young man named Faraday; he has been attending my lectures, and wants me to give him employment at the Royal Institution—what *can* I do?' 'Do?' replied Pepys, 'put him to wash bottles;

Entry into the Service of Science

if he is good for anything he will do it directly; if he refuses, he is good for nothing.' 'No, no,' answered Sir Humphry, 'we must try him with something better than that.'

The same day, having thought over the matter carefully, he writes to Mr. Faraday, Weymouth Street, Portland Place, as follows:

'I am far from displeased with the proof you have given me of your confidence, which displays great zeal, power of memory, and attention. I am obliged to go out of Town, and shall not be settled in town till the end of January. I will then see you at any time you wish. It would gratify me to be of any service to you; I wish it may be in my power.'

Did Sir Humphry's footman deliver this letter (the walk would take him only a few minutes) without delay? If so, what a wonderful Christmas present it would be for Michael! Before, however, we examine what happened when he finally appeared for interview, it is necessary to tell how he had been faring during the intervening few months.

He had left Davy's lecture-room under an irrevocable spell. Never again could he endure the prospect of being a bookbinder all his life, he knew himself ordained to become a servant of science. A very humble servant, the disciple and assistant of a real scientist like Davy—that was the pinnacle of his ambition, but how to achieve it? His apprenticeship was due to expire that autumn, and he must take some action before then. The obvious course was to go straight to headquarters and beseech the aid of Sir Humphry himself, but by the time he had plucked up courage to do so Sir Humphry and his bride had left for a protracted honeymoon tour in Scotland, and he was informed they were not due to return to London until December. In desperation, he addressed an appeal to Sir Joseph Banks, President of the Royal Society of

London, but was bluntly told by the butler when he called again: 'No reply'.

Meanwhile, he rewrote with consummate accuracy his notes on Davy's lectures, and could not resist the urge to impart his conviction of the gospel truth of all Davy's principles to his own friends and effect their conversion. To Abbott particularly he sent during that summer reams and reams regarding Davy's revolutionary views on chlorine—how it could not be a compound substance containing oxygen as everybody had hitherto believed, but must be considered a true element. When Abbott ventured to put forward some tentative objections—it may be stressed that the question remained a matter of acute conflict for several years before all Davy's opponents threw in the sponge—Faraday felt that he himself must have been remiss in his exposition, and bombarded the unfortunate Abbott with new arguments until he was begged to desist.

On 8th October 1812, the day after he was free from his indentures, he went, probably on Masquerier's recommendation, as a journeyman bookbinder to Mr. De La Roche, another French refugee in London. De La Roche was a man of fiery temper, and gave his assistant so much provocation that Michael felt he could not remain in his employ. It is likely that De La Roche had some reason for resentment, since Michael's heart was evidently not in his work. He found he had even less liberty and time for scientific studies than before, and in the letter to Huxtable cited at the beginning of this chapter he betrays his chagrin at his rebuff by Sir Joseph Banks and his low spirits at Sir Humphry Davy's continued absence.

If he had only known it, Humphry was back in London before the end of that month, even Lady Davy and his favourite sport of fishing could not prevail against the still stronger call of chemistry. He had actually taken a portable chemical chest with him on his honeymoon tour, and had done some preliminary work in Edinburgh on a new compound of chlorine and nitrogen reported to him by his friend Ampère in Paris—a highly explosive fluid which had cost its discoverer, Dulong, an eye and a finger. His portable apparatus proving insufficient for its manufacture, Davy hurried south, and very nearly succeeded in duplicating Dulong's experience. He reported to Lady Davy that he had had 'a slight accident'; in fact, as already noted, it was really serious and he was incapacitated from experimental work for some months. Michael heard the good and the bad news when he inquired at the Royal Institution in December, and wisely decided not to disturb the wounded warrior by a personal visit immediately. Let him disclose his plan of campaign in his own words:

'My desire to escape from trade, which I thought vicious and selfish, and to enter into the service of Science, which I imagined made its pursuers amiable and liberal, induced me at last to take the bold and simple step of writing to Sir H. Davy expressing my wishes, and a hope that, if an opportunity came in his way, he would favour my views; at the same time, I sent the notes I had taken of his lectures.'

The result of this 'bold and simple step' has already been narrated.

In January 1813, Humphry invited Michael to come to the Royal Institution for an interview; this took place 'by the window which is nearest to the corridor, or in the ante-room to the lecture-theatre'. Exactly what was said is not recorded, but we can envisage the ingenuous Michael, under Humphry's questioning, divulging not only his innermost aspirations but also his mother's poverty and his desire to help her. He could not have taken a better line to enlist Humphry's sympathy, for the great man himself had known penury and could vividly remember how his own mother had been obliged, after his father's death, to let rooms to lodgers. He had no immediate vacancy, however, to offer his young visitor, and frankly advised him to retain his employment as a bookbinder for the time being, promising to send him all the books the Royal Institution needed to have bound, as well as his own and those of his friends with whom he had influence. Michael must have impressed him very favourably indeed, for when a short time later his eyesight became temporarily worse he engaged him for a few days to function as his secretary.

Then the pendulum of fortune swung at last in Michael's favour. An unprecedented event occurred at the Royal Institution. Mr. Newman, the instrument-maker, and Mr. Payne, Davy's assistant, had a quarrel. Mr. Payne lost his temper and assaulted Mr. Newman; the Managers resolved that the offender should be dismissed immediately. The story may be continued by an extract from Bence Jones:

'One night, when undressing in Weymouth Street, Faraday was startled by a loud knock at the door; and on looking out he saw a carriage from which the footman had alighted and left a note for him. This was a request from Sir H. Davy that he would call on him the next morning. Sir H. Davy then referred to their former interview, and inquired whether he was still in the same mind, telling him that if so he would give him the place of assistant in the laboratory of the Royal Institution, from which he had on the previous day ejected its former occupant. The salary was to be 25 shillings a week, with two rooms at the top of the house.'

In the minutes of the meeting of managers on 1st March 1813, is this entry: 'Sir Humphry Davy has the honour to inform the managers that he has found a person who is desirous to occupy the situation in the Institution lately filled by William Payne. His name is Michael Faraday. He is a youth of twenty-two years of age. As far as Sir H. Davy has been able to observe or ascertain, he appears well fitted for the situation. His habits seem good, his disposition active and cheerful, and his manner intelligent. He is willing to engage himself on the same terms as those given to Mr. Payne at the time of quitting the Institution.

'Resolved—That Michael Faraday be engaged to fill the situation lately occupied by Mr. Payne on the same terms.'

This account may be amplified by Faraday's own report:

'At the same time that he thus gratified my desires as to scientific employment, he still advised me not to give up the prospects I had before me, telling me that Science was a harsh mistress; and in a pecuniary point of view but poorly rewarding those who devoted themselves to her service. He smiled at my notion of the superior moral feelings of philosophic men, and said he would leave me to the experience of a few years to set me right on that matter.'

Mark well those words; Michael certainly could not complain, in later life, that he had not been warned! De La Roche, also, did his utmost to induce him to remain in his employment; in spite of his acid temperament, he had a genuine liking for his young assistant, and even said to him: 'I have no child, and if you will stay with me you shall have all I have when I am gone.' But nothing could change Michael's decision; he was not only entering the service of science, he was to be in daily attendance on his scientific idol. His happiness was complete; he walked on air. How attractive a prospect stretched out before his imagination!

The reality, during the next few weeks, contained few dull moments. True, there is no record that Michael was called upon by Davy to participate in the attempts he was then making to isolate chlorine's sister element, fluorine, from its compounds by the electric current, attempts that he was finally forced to abandon because of the effect of the fumes of hydrofluoric acid on his nails and eyes. No, Michael's first letter to his friend Abbott after his installation merely reports that he had had a finger ('I can't say a hand, for I did very little') in a lecture by Mr. Powell on rotatory motion ('a pretty good lecture, but not very fully attended') and that he was busy extracting sugar from beetroot and preparing a compound of sulphur and carbon. But Humphry now reverted, with his usual disregard for danger, to his attack on nitrogen trichloride—he was vainly hoping to achieve the disintegration of nitrogen with its aid—and Michael immediately undergoes a regular blitz, as he writes to Abbott on April 9th:

'I have escaped (not quite unhurt) from four different and strong explosions of the substance. Of these the most terrible was when I was holding between my thumb and finger a small tube containing $7\frac{1}{2}$ grains of it. My face was within twelve inches of the tube; but I fortunately had on a glass mask. The explosion was so rapid as to blow my hand open, tear off a part of one nail, and has made my fingers so sore that I cannot yet use them easily. The pieces of tube were projected with such force as to cut the glass face of the mask I had on. On repeating the experiment this morning the tube and a receiver were blown to pieces. I got a cut on my eyelid, and Sir H. bruised his hand. The experiment was repeated again with a larger portion of the substance. It stood for a moment or two, and then exploded with a fearful noise: both Sir H. and I had masks on, but I escaped this time the best. Sir H. had his face cut in two places about the chin, and a violent blow on the forehead struck through a considerable thickness of silk and leather; and with this experiment he has for the present concluded.'

In his new environment, he does not forget his old friends. Earlier that year, he had joined the City Philosophical Society, which consisted of thirty or forty individuals, all of humble or moderate rank, who met at Mr. Tatum's house every Wednesday evening for mutual instruction. During the spring half a dozen of the members of the society, including its secretary, Magrath, who had first met Michael in his Riebau days, also began to hold meetings on Saturday nights, usually in Faraday's room in the attic of the Royal Institution, —a practice continued for several years. And in May Michael introduces a human touch into one of his letters to Abbott:

'You must know, Sir, that there is a grand party at dinner at Jacques' Hotel, which immediately faces the back of the Institution; and the music is so excellent, that I cannot for the life of me help running at every new piece they play to the window to hear them. I shall do no good at this letter to-night, and so will go to bed, and "listen, listen to the voice of" bassoons, violins, clarionettes, trumpets, serpents, and all the accessories to good music. I can't stop. Good-night.'

In June he starts to inflict upon his favourite friend an extraordinary series of letters on the art of lecturing. He discusses in detail lecture-rooms, lectures, apparatus, diagrams, experiments, audiences; his remarks on all these topics show the keenness of his observation, the abundance of his ideas, and the soundness of his judgment, and it is noteworthy that he writes without the slightest premonition of his own future fame. One phrase only can be quoted here: 'I disapprove of long lectures; one hour is enough for anyone.'

In September, however, new exciting vistas appear on his horizon. Writing to an uncle and aunt in Clapham, he announces:

Entry into the Service of Science

'I have lately had proposals made to me by Sir Humphry Davy to accompany him, in his travels through Europe and into Asia, as philosophical assistant. If I go at all I expect it will be in October next, about the end, and my absence from home will perhaps be as long as three years. But as yet all is uncertain.' His prospective duties are more clearly defined in a later letter to Abbott:

'When Sir Humphry first made proposals to me to accompany him in the voyage, he told me that I should be occupied in assisting him in his experiments, in taking care of the apparatus, and of his papers and books, and in writing, and other things of this kind; and I, conceiving that such employment, with the opportunities that travelling would present, would tend greatly to instruct me in what I desired to know and in things useful in life, consented to go.'

How could this contemplated journey be possible? Great Britain and France were then at death-grips, national animosity was extreme, Napoleon still held as prisoners all the British trapped on the Continent when hostilities were resumed after the brief Peace of Amiens in 1802. Nevertheless the Emperor, always an enthusiastic patron of science, made a special dispensation in Sir Humphry's favour, and that October a party of four—Sir Humphry and Lady Davy, Faraday and Lady Davy's maid—proceeded by coach to Plymouth, their port of embarkation.

The party should have been five, but at the last minute Sir Humphry's valet, Le Fontaine (a refugee from Flanders, who spoke both French and Italian), was persuaded by his weeping wife not to run the risk of putting himself in the power of the Corsican ogre, who was reputed to feed on human flesh. War propaganda was evidently just as prevalent in the nineteenth century as in the twentieth. Michael remarks: 'When Sir H. informed me of this circumstance, he expressed his sorrow at it, and said he had not time to find another to suit him, but that if I would put up with a few things on the road, until he got to Paris, doing those things which could not be trusted to strangers or waiters, and which Le Fontaine would have done, he would there get a servant, which would leave me at liberty to fill my proper station and that alone. I felt unwilling to proceed on this plan; but considering the advantages I should lose, and the short time I should be thus embarrassed, I agreed.'

The simplicity and imprudence of Michael in consenting to this 'temporary' arrangement will emerge immediately.

CHAPTER THREE

Scientific Assistant or Valet?

It is the name more than the thing which hurts.
MICHAEL FARADAY (1814)

It is 14th April 1814, and a young wanderer is writing to his mother from Rome. So long as he was in enemy territory, communication had been impossible, but now Napoleon has fallen and Faraday finds himself in 'a land of friends'. By a high favour Sir Humphry will put this letter with his own London mail, and it will be conveyed 'by a particular person'. It is much too long to reproduce in full, but here are a few extracts from it.

'I trust that you are well in health and spirits, and that all things have gone right since I left you. The first and last thing in my mind is England, home and friends. When Sir H. Davy first had the goodness to ask me whether I would go with him, I mentally said: "No, I have a mother, I have relations." Now I am glad that I have left some behind me on whom I can think, and whose actions and occupations I can picture in my mind. Whenever a vacant hour occurs, whenever present circumstances are disagreeable, the thoughts of those at home are a warm and refreshing balm to my heart.

'I have said nothing as yet to you, dear mother, about our past journey, which has been as pleasant (a few things excepted, in reality nothing) as it is possible to be. I have crossed the Alps and the Apennines; I have been at the

39

Jardin des Plantes; at the museum arranged by Buffon; at the Louvre, among the masterpieces of sculpture and painting; at the Luxembourg palace, among Rubens' works; I have seen a GLOW-WORM!!!, water-spouts, torpedo [electric eel], the museum at the Academy del Cimento, as well as St. Peter's, some of the antiquities here, and a vast variety of things far too numerous to mention.

'At present I am in very good health, and so far is travelling from disagreeing with me that I am become somewhat heavier and thicker than when I left England. We have heard this morning that Paris was taken by the Allied Troops on March 31st. Englishmen are here respected almost to adoration, and I proudly own myself as belonging to that nation which holds so high a place in the scale of European powers.

'Adieu, dear Mother, at present. Your dutiful son,

'Michael.'

The paramount point in this letter is where Michael lets a hint escape that his bed has not been entirely a bed of roses. He is thoughtful enough not to worry his mother unduly with his troubles—he tells her that they are 'in reality nothing'—but in subsequent letters to his friends he is much more outspoken. Writing to Abbott from Geneva in September he confesses: 'If I could have foreseen the things that have passed, I should never have left London. I have several times been more than half decided to return hastily home.'

What was it that almost compelled Michael to break away from his benefactor and to believe that, on his return to England he would have to resume, for a time at least, his old profession of bookbinder? The answer is, briefly: *Cherchez la femme*! A dark woman had crossed his path; Lady Davy— that 'brunette of brunettes', that 'piece of brown toast', as Sydney Smith entitled her—had turned his day to night. The story is pried out of Michael by degrees in reply to anxious inquiries from Abbott; a very condensed version of it follows.

It will be recalled that Sir Humphry had expressly promised to obtain a replacement for the faint-hearted Le Fontaine as soon as Paris was reached, so that Michael might be relieved of his extra duties as valet. Now let Michael tell what actually happened:

'At Paris he could find no servant to suit him, for he wished for one that spoke English, French, and a little German (I speaking no French at that time), and as all the English there (ourselves excepted) were prisoners, and none of the French servants talked English, our want remained unsupplied. At Lyons he could not get one; at Montpellier he could not get one; nor at Genoa, nor at Florence, nor at Rome, nor in all Italy; and I believe at last he did not wish to get one: and we are just the same now as we were when we left England. This of course throws things into my duty which it was not my agreement, and is not my wish, to perform, but which are, if I remain with Sir H., unavoidable. These, it is true, are very few; for having been accustomed in early years to do for himself, he continues to do so at present, and he leaves very little for a valet to perform; and as he knows that it is not pleasing to me, and that I do not consider myself as obliged to do them, he is always as careful as possible to keep those things from me which he knows would be disagreeable. But Lady Davy is of another humour. She likes to show her authority, and at first I found her extremely earnest in mortifying me. This occasioned quarrels between us, at each of which I gained ground, and she lost it; for the frequency made me care nothing about them, and weakened her authority, and after each she behaved in a milder manner. I should have but little to complain of were I travelling with Sir Humphry alone, or were Lady Davy like him; but her temper makes it oftentimes go wrong with me, with herself, and with Sir H. . . .'

In justice to Lady Davy, it must be mentioned that we do not know her side of the story, and she might quite easily put up a very plausible reply. It must have been extremely galling for her to find her distinguished husband continually occupied with experimental work—the portable chemical chest he had taken on their honeymoon accompanied him everywhere on his continental tour—when she wanted him to escort her to important social engagements like a visit to the Empress Marie Louise. She must have found it impossible to understand why the sanctimonious menial he had picked out of the gutter (she was, to put it mildly, extremely class-conscious) should not relieve him entirely of such drudgery. As she gradually became conscious of the fact that Humphry's love for science took precedence of his love for her, her resentment would naturally fall upon the unlucky Michael and she would 'put him in his proper place' at every possible opportunity. The poor lady deserves, indeed, some pity, although we cannot for an instant regret Sir Humphry's protection of his young protégé against her tantrums, since the salvation of Michael's scientific career outweighs a millionfold the shipwreck of her matrimonial bliss.

Sir Humphry himself, of course, cannot be absolved from blame in the matter; he should have found *some* way of redeeming his promise to Michael. Even though he did defend him against Lady Davy, he had not the slightest conception then—nor, as we shall see, for many years afterwards—what a priceless boon he was bestowing upon humanity by so doing. His motives were essentially personal; Michael was indispensable to him as an extra pair of hands in the investigations he was conducting during his travels. Without Michael's assistance it is unlikely that he would have been

Scientific Assistant or Valet?

able to win his spectacular race against the French chemists in the identification of iodine as a new element (page 49), and Humphry's nature was such that he could not bear to be beaten at anything.

Michael's dogged devotion to Sir Humphry must have made this victory just as pleasing to him as to his master; how could he leave such a champion? This continental tour, in point of fact, was providing him with the equivalent of the college education that he had missed. In the company of Sir Humphry, he was constantly sharpening his intellect against the best brains of Europe. As he wrote to Abbott from Geneva: 'I have learned just enough to perceive my ignorance, and, ashamed of my defects in everything, I wish to seize the opportunity of remedying them. The little knowledge I have gained in languages makes me wish to know more of them, and the little I have seen of men and manners is just enough to make me desirous of seeing more; added to which, the glorious opportunity I enjoy of improving in the knowledge of chemistry and the sciences continually determines me to finish this voyage with Sir Humphry Davy. But if I wish to enjoy those advantages, I have to sacrifice much; and though those sacrifices are such as an humble man would not feel, yet I cannot quietly make them.'

Lest any reader should suspect that Michael was super-sensitive and was making mountains out of molehills, a final incident that occurred at Geneva, where Sir Humphry's party were the guests of the celebrated scientist De La Rive, may be related:

'Host and guest were sportsmen, and they frequently went out shooting. On these occasions Faraday loaded Davy's gun, and for a time he had his meals with the servants. From nature Faraday had received the warp and woof of a gentleman, and this, added to his bright intelligence, soon led De

43

La Rive to the discovery that he was Davy's laboratory assistant, not his servant. Somewhat shocked at the discovery, De La Rive proposed that Faraday should dine with the family, instead of with the domestics. To this Lady Davy demurred, and De La Rive met the case by sending Faraday's meals to his own room.' One version of the story makes De La Rive remark: 'Now I shall have to eat *two* dinners!' Whether he actually did so or not, the fact remains that he became firm friends with Faraday, and a lively correspondence, which began with the father, was continued by his equally famous son, lasting altogether nearly fifty years. Bence Jones states: 'There was no one to whom Faraday wrote an account of his work and of his thoughts with so much pleasure and so much sympathy as to his friend De La Rive.'

Michael's boyish affability and natural manner, indeed, enforced universal affection from all his continental hosts. On the other hand, Sir Humphry's assumption of inherent superiority—he was tactless enough to let Napoleon know that he thought the French chemists were a poor lot—antagonized many; they fully admitted his genius but did not relish his arrogance. One of the greatest of the next generation, Jean Baptiste Dumas, after touching upon the censure Davy kindled by his discourtesy, proceeds to record: 'His laboratory assistant, long before he had won his great celebrity by his works, had by his modesty, his amiability, and his intelligence, gained most devoted friends at Paris, at Geneva, at Montpellier. Amongst these may be named in the front rank M. De La Rive, the distinguished chemist, father of the illustrious physicist. The kindnesses with which he covered my youth contributed not a little to unite us—Faraday and myself. With pleasure we used to recall that we made one another's acquaintance under the auspices of that affectionate and helpful philosopher whose example so truly witnessed that science does not dry up the heart's blood. At Montpellier, beside the hospitable hearth of Bérard, the associate of Chaptal, Faraday has left memories equally charged with an undying sympathy which his master could never have inspired. We admired Davy, we loved Faraday.'

All through his travels, Michael kept a comprehensive journal. Having unloaded him of his main burden, we can now let him lead us with lighter feet over the route of his pilgrim's progress.

CHAPTER FOUR

The Grand Tour of Europe

The continued talk and chatter of people together when they are at work, whether in the house, or in the street, or in the air, as upon some of their cathedral scaffolds, is quite remarkable. The French must be a very thinking race to have so much to say.

MICHAEL FARADAY

The above comment was actually made by Michael during a much later visit to Paris, but it is characteristic of him at any age; he always exhibited the same simple sense of humour. His Journal of 1813–1815, however, begins soberly enough: 'This morning formed a new epoch in my life. I have never before, within my recollection, left London at a greater distance than twelve miles; and now I leave it perhaps for many years, and to visit spots between which and home whole realms will intervene. 'Tis indeed a strange venture at this time, to trust ourselves in a foreign and hostile country, where also so little regard is had to protestations and honour, that the slightest suspicion would be sufficient to separate us for ever from England, and perhaps from life.'

The party reached Plymouth on October 15th, Devonshire having effected a kind of revolution in Michael's ideas respecting the nature of the earth's surface. 'This day gave me some ideas of the pleasures of travelling, and has raised my expectations of future enjoyment to a very high point.' The

46

swell of the sea during the Channel crossing was considerable, but Michael remained on the deck of the small packet-boat all night, fascinated in watching the luminescence of the water, and escaped sea-sickness. On arrival at Morlaix, a small port near Finisterre, 'a mighty man of office came, attended by several understrappers and a barge-full of Frenchmen, apparently beggars and porters.' All the strangers were subjected in turn to a rigorous examination, even their shoes being searched. 'I could hardly help laughing at the ridiculous nature of their precautions. Our English sailors looked on with pity and indignation.' The letters Michael had written on board and given to the captain of the cartel to be conveyed back to Plymouth were seized, he and his companions—with their bulky luggage, including Sir Humphry's grand coach—were taken on to the barge, and the 'enemy ship' was then given leave to return. 'Certainly it was with no pleasurable feelings I believed myself separated from my countrymen, conscious of the tyrannical and oppressive laws and manners of the people in whose hands we remained.'

What a typical John Bull our Michael is! He resolves, however, to content and amuse himself by looking out for variety, and he finds plenty of that in the customs examination the following morning. Every part of Sir Humphry's carriage is thumped over to discover hollow and secret places, stockings that are new are threatened with confiscation, and the business ends only with a gift to the officers for 'their *polite* attention.' The hotel at which the travellers were forced to tarry for several days—they were detained as suspects until confirmation of their credentials arrived from Paris—was the best in Morlaix, but Michael is horrified by its kitchen, cluttered up by all the idlers, beggars, and nondescripts of the town. 'I think it is impossible for an English person to eat the things that come out of this place, except through ignorance or actual and impressive hunger, and yet in some cases their dishes are to the taste excellent and inviting.'

When they leave Morlaix on October 22nd, the postilion excites tremendous interest. His jackboots (which weigh between fourteen and twenty pounds), his whip (with a thong six to eight feet in length, constantly in a state of violent vibratory motion over the heads of the horses) and his elaborate tobacco-pouch all come in for minute description. The 300-mile journey to Paris occupies nearly a week; one night a minor mishap occurs and, while the postilion is putting matters right, Michael sees and picks up his first GLOW-WORM!!! (see page 40). But what he admires most of all are the French pigs. 'At first I was positively doubtful of their nature, for though they have pointed noses, long ears, rope-like tails, and cloven feet, yet who would have imagined that an animal with a long thin body, capable of outrunning our horses for a mile or two together, could be at all allied to the fat sow of England? I find that what at a distance I should judge to be a greyhound I am obliged, at a near approach, to acknowledge a pig.'

Paris also he finds bewildering. 'The streets are paved with equality—that is to say, no difference is made in them between men and beasts, and no part of the street is reserved for either.' He determines to exert himself to learn French, but has trouble in securing a suitable grammar, owing to the long lack of communication with England; finally he purchases one composed for Americans. He calls at Police Headquarters for a passport, only by paying for the information can he find the office he wants in the enormous building, but once arrived he arouses universal curiosity, since except for Sir Humphry Davy there is not another free Englishman on the register. An American present can scarcely believe his senses, 'and would willingly have been mightily inquisitive'; Michael does not seem to realize that the United States at that time was also at war with Great Britain. He is put down on the books as possessing 'a round chin, a brown beard, a large mouth, a great nose, etc., etc.'; then they give him his passport and let him go.

He visits the Louvre, and describes it as 'the glory and the disgrace of France. Its works of art are unsurpassed, unequalled, and must call forth the highest and most unqualified admiration; but when memory brings to mind the manner in which they came here, and views them only as the gains of violence and rapine, she blushes for the people that even now glory in an act that made them a nation of thieves.' He visits some of the churches, but is not induced to stop long in any of them. 'It could hardly be expected that they would have attractions for a tasteless heretic.'

But on November 23rd his period of leisure ends. That morning Davy's friend, Ampère, greatly to the subsequent indignation of his colleagues, presents him with a sample of a mysterious substance X, recently extracted from seaweed. For three weeks Davy, with Michael's help, works feverishly upon it and establishes that it is an element with properties analagous to chlorine. He gives it the name of iodine, and bitter controversy ensues between him and Gay-Lussac, who had been pursuing parallel investigations.[1] Davy is no longer *persona grata* in the French capital, and preparations are made for departure.

Before leaving Paris, however, Michael hears Gay-Lussac lecture, and waits one day in very bad weather on the terrace of the Tuileries to watch Napoleon pass in full state in a procession to the Senate. 'He was sitting in one corner of his

[1] This topic is discussed in detail in *Humphry Davy: 'Pilot' of Penzance.*

carriage, covered and almost hidden from sight by an enormous robe of ermine, and his face overshadowed by a tremendous plume of feathers that descended from a velvet hat. A numerous guard surrounded him. No acclamation was heard where I stood, and no comments.' The Allied net was rapidly closing round a France that had been bled white by the Emperor's ambition.

On December 29th Sir Humphry's carriage starts southwards, and Michael prepares himself for new experiences. 'The morning was fine, but very cold and frosty; but on entering the forest of Fontainebleau we did not regret the severity of the weather, for I do not think I ever saw a more beautiful scene. Every small twig and every blade of herbage was encrusted by a splendid coat of hoar frost, the crystals of which in most cases extended above half an inch.' Humphry was inspired to write one of his polished poems, but Michael's plain prose is just as impressive.

Montpellier is reached on 8th January 1814. 'I believe we shall remain here some time. The town seems to be very pretty; but the hotel we are in must not be compared to that at Lyons, except for good oil and wine, and good-nature in all the persons in it.' The month spent at Montpellier, in fact, saw Humphry and Michael continuing to work very closely on iodine, and when the Pope passed through the place one morning Michael records: 'almost every person in the town was there but myself.'

On February 17th the party leaves Nice and, two days after, makes the dangerous passage of the Col de Tende into Italy. Michael takes no chances: 'expecting it to be very cold, I added to my ordinary clothing an extra waistcoat, two pairs of stockings, and a nightcap.' He is later constrained to confess: 'the sun darted his burning rays with much force upon us, so as even to make us throw off our greatcoats, though encompassed by fields of snow and ice.' A band of no fewer than sixty-five people precedes the coach, to help when its wheels become blocked in the snowdrifts; Michael finds something pleasant in the appearance of their chief, whose clothing, like that of his underlings, 'consisted of few articles'. The road suddenly ends, the carriage is dismantled and loaded in sections on two sledges and five mules, and Michael climbs and scrambles along a very narrow and precipitous path, holding a barometer in his hand. If he is still wearing his nightcap, he must distract Lady Davy's attention from her own predicament—she is being carried in a sedan chair which, as Michael notes, is often placed in a position nearly vertical from the steepness of the ascent. Half-way up the mountain Michael, very comfortably warm, finds the mule and sledge trains waiting in a ruined house for their leader and the dram-bottle. After a short rest the climb is resumed, and at precisely 3.43 p.m. Michael reaches the summit, more than 6,000 feet above sea-level; Sir Humphry's barometer stands at 25·3 inches (the mercury in Michael's instrument has sunk below the scale) and the thermometer registers 11° Fahrenheit. Could scientific accuracy be carried further?

The descent through still deeper drifts of snow proves more dangerous, although not so tiring. One mule rolls down the mountainside, but is rescued. 'Just as starlight came on, the sounds of the evening bell of a distant village were faintly heard. We got to Leman about seven o'clock and there put up for the night; supper and rest being both welcome.'

Turin is reached in time for Michael to witness the celebrations on the last day of Carnival, and he is hugely diverted. At Genoa he attends the opera: 'The theatre was small and pretty; the performance to me very tedious.' He also participates in some experiments with Humphry on torpedoes [electric eels]: 'the great object was to ascertain whether water could be decomposed by the electrical power possessed by these animals. No effect was perceived. However, the smallness and weakness of the fish and the coldness of the season prevented any negative conclusion from being formed.' Michael consoles himself by running to the seashore during a violent thunderstorm to watch three water-spouts.

In March, a halt is made at Florence; Michael goes with Humphry to the Academy del Cimento, where he views with immense interest Galileo's first telescope, the great burning-glass of the Grand Duke of Tuscany, and an enormous magnet supporting a weight of 150 pounds. He spends several days assisting Humphry in more work on iodine, and then collaborates in 'the grand experiment of burning the diamond'. A series of such experiments—which Michael describes in detail—enables Humphry to communicate a paper to the Royal Society of London establishing the important result that 'the diamond is pure carbon'.

Next month the party reaches Rome, and Michael sees all the sights of 'that city of wonders, but wonders created by a former nation and in a former age'. He marvels at an experiment he beholds on the attempted conversion of an ordinary needle into a magnet by means of the solar rays, little dreaming of the eternal renown that the study of magnetism and light is fated to bring him. In May he moves on to Naples, and on Friday the thirteenth (fortunately he is not superstitious) records: 'Mount Vesuvius was the employment of today, and fully rewarded the trouble and fatigue attendant on seeing it.' One of the main objects of Sir Humphry's tour was to investigate volcanoes, regarding which he held very unorthodox views, and he kindly explains to Michael, stand-

ing at the edge of the crater, various points in connection
with the violent eruption then in progress. Michael is so impressed that he incautiously remains to collect some speci-
mens of minerals indicated to him, the wind suddenly
changes and to escape suffocation he is obliged to run over
the lava, to the great danger of his legs. Nothing daunted,
however, he takes part in a second ascent on Saturday. A
later start is made, with the intention of seeing the crater at
night, and Michael gives a graphic description of 'the dreadful place in all its horrors'. Before descending, he joins in 'a
species of dinner' spread on cloths laid on the smoking lava
and sings 'God save the King' and 'Rule Britannia' at the
conclusion of the eerie banquet.

Now the expedition retraces its course northwards to visit
Switzerland. At Terni Michael catches several fire-flies and
makes experiments and speculations on the cause of their
'transient light'. At Milan he meets Volta, the doyen of
electricity, 'who came to Sir H. Davy, a hale elderly man,
bearing the red ribbon, and very free in conversation'. The
summer is spent at Geneva, where Michael resumes his study
of luminosity by work on glow-worms and catches up with
his correspondence. He finds 'the constant presence of Sir
Humphry Davy a mine inexhaustible of knowledge and improvement', he continues to assist him in his investigations
on iodine and the prismatic spectrum, but he also tells
Abbott in September: 'Our time has been employed lately in
fishing and shooting; and many a quail has been killed in the
plains of Geneva, and many trout and grayling have been
pulled out of the Rhône.'

A long excursion next through Berne, Zurich, the Falls of
the Rhine at Schaffhausen, Munich and many other towns in
Southern Germany, to the Tyrol and Venice. To his mother
Michael writes an exquisite description of Venice, beginning:

'You will remember very well, I have no doubt, the picture which hung in the parlour over the fireplace, and which represented the Rialto and the Grand Canal.' How she must have treasured this testimony of his remembrance! Michael always enjoyed harking back to his early days; he never fails to ask his mother to give his regards to Mr. Riebau, and he even begs Abbott to convey his gratitude to Mr. De La Roche, who has been acting the Good Samaritan to her in his absence.

During the crossing of the Apennines on the return journey to Florence, nothing can deter Davy, though it is raining hard, from making a halt to inspect a remarkable phenomenon—great quantities of combustible gas bursting out of cracks in the soil and boiling up through pools. Michael collects some of the gas and, in the laboratory of the Florentine Academy, it is submitted to careful analysis. The results indicate that it is pure 'light hydrocarburet', known to miners as fire-damp and now called methane. This same gas is going to demand much more serious attention when the travellers get back to England, as we shall presently see.

Once more in Rome for the winter, Michael indulges in an orgy of letter-writing—to his mother ('I am always in health, generally contented, and often happy'), to his married sister Elizabeth ('I shall never feel *quite* happy till I get amongst you again'), to his younger sister Margaret ('Your writing is not improved quite so much as I expected'), to Mr. Riebau (acknowledging his humble gratitude for past kindness, and informing him of the state of the book trade on the Continent), to Huxtable ('Sir H. Davy has made his route as scientific as possible; he has not been idle in experimental chemistry; his example did great things in urging the Parisian chemists to exertion'), and above all to Abbott. Most of this long correspondence with his favourite friend deals with personal troubles discussed in the preceding chapter, but the spirit of youth pops out in one postscript: 'Le donne Italiene sono sfacciate, pigrissime e sporchissime. Como dunque volete fare una comparazione fra loro e l'Inglese? Addio, caro amico!'

Did Michael always find the Italian ladies 'pert, indolent and oh, so naughty'? He appears to have joined in the gaieties of Carnival pretty freely, for his journal records on 30th January 1815: 'Went in a domino to a masked ball, and was much amused.' On February 6th another masked ball: 'I stopped there till daylight, and then came home.' The following day demands more extended comment: 'To-night's ball was the last of the profane pleasures the season allowed, and indeed it was well enjoyed. I found all Rome there, and all the English besides. It was too full for dancing, and the amusement was principally the jokes of those that were not known to those whom they knew. I was in a nightgown and nightcap, and had a lady with me whom I had not seen till that night, but who knew all my acquaintances; and between us we puzzled them mightily, and we both came away well entertained.'

What a gay dog this simple Mr. Faraday fancies himself to be! My own suspicion is that his mysterious partner was none other than Lady Davy—who would certainly remember his nightcap—so well disguised that he failed to recognize her under her mask. If so, how she must have enjoyed telling the tale to her friends afterwards!

Sir Humphry, however, sees to it that Michael does not have much free time for dissipation: 'as is the practice with him, he goes on discovering.' That winter, with Michael's collaboration, he completes three separate researches, one on the colours used in ancient Greek and Roman paintings, and two on new compounds of iodine and chlorine with oxygen.

The Grand Tour of Europe

Michael loyally records: 'The discovery of these bodies contradicts many parts of Gay-Lussac's paper on iodine, which has been very much vaunted in these parts. The French chemists were not aware of the importance of the subject until it was shown to them, and now they are in haste to reap all the honours attached to it; but their haste opposes their aim. They reason theoretically, without demonstrating experimentally, and errors are the result.' Subsequent investigators, however, found several flaws in Humphry's own too-hurried conclusions.

The Cornish wizard always worked with lightning rapidity, but just now he had special reasons for speed; he was planning to extend his travels to Sicily, Greece and Turkey. Michael informs his mother on February 15th: 'I can tell you to a moral certainty that we are to see Constantinople.' A week later he writes to Abbott: 'At this moment there is no knowing which way we shall turn. Sir H. intended to see Greece and Turkey this summer, and arrangements were half made for the voyage; but he has just learned that a quarantine must be performed on the road there, and to this he has an utter aversion, and that alone will perhaps break up the journey.'

In point of fact, the party only got as far south as Naples. Michael makes a significant note in his Journal on March 7th: 'I heard for news that Bonaparte was again at liberty. Being no politician, I did not trouble myself much about it, though I suppose it will have a strong influence on the affairs of Europe.' How strong an influence Napoleon's escape from Elba will exert on his own affairs our detached philosopher does not immediately realize. Humphry tarries for two weeks in Naples, where Michael does some more mountaineering with him. They part company half-way, since Humphry wants to see Monte Somma only, while Michael wishes to go

The Grand Tour of Europe

right to the top of Vesuvius again and finds it in fiercer eruption than ever. Then, suddenly, Humphry decides to dash home. On April 16th Michael concludes his Journal with a letter to his mother from Brussels:

My very dear Mother,

It is with no small pleasure I write you my last letter from a foreign country, and I hope it will be with as much pleasure you will hear I am within three days of England. Nay more, before you read this letter I hope to tread on British ground.

I am not aquainted with the reason of our sudden return; it is, however, sufficient for me that it has taken place. We left Naples hastily, we came rapidly to Rome, we as rapidly left it. We ran up Italy, we crossed the Tyrol, we stepped over Germany, we entered Holland, and we are now at Brussels, and talk of leaving it to-morrow for Ostend; at Ostend we embark, and at Deal we land on a spot of earth which I will never leave again. You may be sure we shall not creep from Deal to London, and I am sure I shall not creep to Weymouth Street; and then—but it is of no use. I have a thousand times endeavoured to fancy a meeting with you and my relations and friends, and I am sure I have as often failed: the reality must be a pleasure not to be imagined nor to be described.

I come home almost like the prodigal, for I shall want everything.

Adieu till I see you, dearest Mother; and believe me ever your affectionate and dutiful son,

M. FARADAY.

'Tis the shortest and (to me) the sweetest letter I ever wrote to you.

CHAPTER FIVE

The Hare and the Tortoise

What is the pest and plague of human life?
And what the curse that often brings a wife?
      'Tis Love.
What is the power that ruins man's firmest mind?
What that deceives its host, alas! too kind?
What is't that comes in false deceitful guise,
Making dull fools of those that 'fore were wise?
      'Tis Love.
What is't that oft to an enemy turns a friend?
What is't that promising never attains its end?
What that the wisest head can never scan,
Which seems to have come on earth to humble man?
      'Tis Love.
What is't directs the madman's hot intent,
For which a dunce is fully competent?
What's that the wise man always strives to shun,
Though still it ever o'er the world has run?
      'Tis Love.

MICHAEL FARADAY

Bless your simplicity, Mr. Faraday! could you not foresee, when you wrote this little poem shortly after your return to England, home *and beauty*, that you would be called upon to recant your opinions after the lapse of a few years? In any case, it is certain that you are not cut out to become a poet, your verses will never rival those of your master, Sir Humphry, even although we must surmise, reading between the halting lines, that Sir Humphry and Lady Davy have inspired them.

58

The Hare and the Tortoise

Back now at the Royal Institution, you are free from Lady Davy at least; her society engagements demand her entire attention. Sir Humphry has also left for a long succession of shooting and fishing parties in Scotland, but before his departure—his conscience presumably pricked him a little— he has arranged for your promotion to the position of assistant in the laboratory and mineralogical collection, and superintendent of the apparatus, at the princely salary of thirty shillings a week.

Some difficulty evidently arose in Michael's occupation of the apartments also allotted to him by this appointment, since a month passed before he was put in possession of them, but on June 27th he informed Abbott: 'The enemy having been completely beaten in the contests that took place, not-withstanding the reinforcements which he endeavoured to bring into action, his party was obliged to quit the spot contested for and retire, and I last night found all hindrances removed, and the place as ready for my reception as the short time would allow of.' In the interim, we may be sure, the prodigal was a welcome guest at Weymouth Street, even although his mother had no fatted calf to kill for him. Indeed, it is not long before he is giving her money out of his aug-mented salary to send his younger sister to boarding-school, and depriving himself of dinner every second day in order to do so. How fortunate it was that he had put on flesh during his travels!

His main duties that summer were to help Humphry's good-natured but uninspiring successor, Mr. Brande, at the Royal Institution, and the capable way in which he performed these duties is evidenced by the contemporary comment that Brande was 'lecturing on velvet'. In September, however, Humphry unexpectedly returned to London to start, with his

The Hare and the Tortoise

incomparable energy, those wonderful investigations on the explosive properties of mixtures of air and methane which resulted in the invention of the miner's safety-lamp, and in the comprehensive account of this work published in 1818 he stated: 'I am myself indebted to Mr. Michael Faraday for much able assistance in the prosecution of my experiments.'

Michael's old admiration for his master was enhanced still further by this grand discovery; he regarded the competitive claim of George Stephenson to the invention as 'a disgraceful subject'. Davy was in fact to him almost a god, as Thompson states: 'He preserved every note and manuscript of Davy's with religious care. He copied out Davy's scrawled researches in a neat clear delicate handwriting, begging only for his pains to be allowed to keep the originals, which he bound in two quarto volumes.' Nevertheless, loyalty to Davy could not induce Michael to deviate from scientific truth. The early models of the safety-lamp were not safe under all circumstances. Davy would never acknowledge this, but Michael, when questioned before a Parliamentary Committee, admitted that in certain conditions an explosion might be propagated through the wire mesh. Davy was indignant, but could not make him budge from his convictions.

It is really amazing to contrast the natures of the two men. Humphry exemplifies perfectly the lines from Milton's *Lycidas*:

> *Fame is the spur that the clear spirit doth raise*
> (*That last infirmity of noble mind*)
> *To scorn delights and live laborious days.*

He raced ahead, disregarding all opposition, like a hare; before he reached the age of thirty he outdistanced every rival. He gloried in his supremacy.

Michael, on the other hand, was quite prepared to play the

part of the tortoise in Aesop's fable; he was content to remain in the rear for years as Humphry's almost anonymous assistant. His first publication had to be practically pushed into the *Quarterly Journal of Science* in 1816; it is an analysis of the native caustic lime of Tuscany, less than two pages in length, preceded by an introduction by the Marquis Ridolfi (who supplied the sample) and followed by some observations from Sir Humphry Davy. Forty years later, the author was still modest enough to remark: 'Sir Humphry Davy gave me the analysis to make as a first attempt in chemistry at a time when my fear was greater than my confidence, and both far greater than my knowledge; at a time also when I had no thought of ever writing an original paper on science. The addition of his own comments and the publication of the paper encouraged me to go on making, from time to time, other slight communications. Their transference from the "Quarterly" into other Journals increased my boldness; and now that forty years have elapsed and I can look back on what the successive communications have led to, I still hope, much as their character has changed, that I have not, either now or forty years ago, been too bold.'

It is almost inconceivable, but the tortoise by now is in first place. He plods on perseveringly, and cannot understand why the onlookers are applauding his endurance. Personal fame means nothing to him, his mind is entirely concentrated on steady progress towards the distant goal.

His slow advance during the period 1815–1821 does not call for extended comment. In 1817, he published six short papers in the *Quarterly Journal of Science*, all originating from his collaboration with Davy on the development of the miner's safety-lamp. In 1818, he had eleven papers in the *Journal*; he is still leaning heavily on Humphry in two that deal with the combustion of the diamond, but he breaks new ground in investigations on the solution of compounds of silver in ammonia and on the action of ammonia on metallic chlorides. His most ambitious effort of the year is an article on 'the singing tubes'; he puts forward a very lucid explanation of the tones produced when jets of combustible gases burn in vessels of most diverse materials and shapes, and even ventures to correct De La Rive's original assertion that the alternate expansion and contraction of water vapour is the cause of the phenomenon. In 1819, he printed nineteen papers in the *Journal*, mostly of minor importance, although he evidently obtained much quiet enjoyment in analysing a number of known metals out of a sample of a supposedly new element, 'Sirium', discovered by an Austrian chemist, and in demonstrating that when this was done he was left with: 'Nothing at all'.

His gradual emancipation from slavish picking-up of Humphry's unconsidered trifles was due, no doubt, to the latter's departure on a second continental journey in the spring of 1818. Humphry's object was to devise new chemical methods for unrolling the manuscripts recently found among the ruins of Herculaneum; he wrote to Michael from Rome in October as follows: 'Mr. Hatchett's letter contained praises of you which were very gratifying to me; for, believe me, there is no one more interested in your success and welfare than your sincere well-wisher and friend, H. Davy.'

In February 1819, Humphry wrote again to Michael: 'I have sent a report on the state of the MSS. to our Government, with a plan for the undertaking of unrolling; one part of the plan is to employ a chemist for the purpose at Naples: should they consent, I hope I shall have to make a proposition to you on the subject.' In May, a third letter: 'It gives me great pleasure to hear that you are comfortable at the Royal Institution, and I trust that you will not only do something

good and honourable for yourself, but likewise for science.'
And in December, a fourth: 'Could you have left the Royal
Institution for a few months or a year, and have been secure
of returning to your situation, I should have strongly recommended to you the employment at Naples. This indeed is still
open, for the person I have engaged as operator is hired by
the month. When I have seen my way a little as to the time
the MS. operations will demand, I will write to you.'

The cold truth is that Humphry was missing Michael's
skilled assistance sadly; things were not going nearly as well
as he expected. Michael, however, evinced no eagerness to
accept the invitation; Lady Davy was with her husband and
he did not propose to put his neck in the same noose twice.
Humphry ultimately had a fierce quarrel with the curators of
the museum and abandoned his investigations.

Meanwhile Michael had communicated his first important
discovery—the existence of two compounds of chlorine and
carbon—to the Royal Society. One of these compounds,
hexachlorethane, is now used extensively in fire-extinguishers.
Another paper, in collaboration with his old friend at Mr.
Tatum's lectures, Phillips, reported upon a third compound
of chlorine and carbon some months later.

A more laborious series of researches on steel alloys,
carried out in conjunction with Stodart, a surgical instrument-
maker, was started in 1818, and continued for several years.
Discussion of the results of this work will be deferred for the
present, since in June 1820 Humphry made his reappearance.
His return coincided with the death of the President of the
Royal Society, Sir Joseph Banks, and a great deal of back-
stage manœuvring ensued before a successor was appointed.
The two main contestants were Davy and Wollaston—one of
the managers of the Royal Institution, a wealthy man distinguished for his work on the platinum metals—but Wollas-

ton finally withdrew and Davy was elected. Both he and Wollaston, as well as Michael and many more, now switched their attention to a striking new scientific development, a development that was eventually to make the name of Faraday immortal, the inter-relation of magnetism and electricity.

This development, like so many others in science, sprang from a very simple discovery, and a chance discovery at that. The full story was disclosed to Faraday in 1857 in a letter from Professor Hansteen of Christiania, who was present when Professor Oersted of Copenhagen early in 1820 performed an experiment which, as Faraday himself remarked: 'burst open the gates of a domain in science, dark till then, and filled it with a flood of light'. Hansteen's English is a little awkward in places, but his original wording has been retained throughout.

'Professor Oersted was a man of genius, but he was a very unhappy experimenter; he could not manipulate instruments. He must always have an assistant, or one of his auditors who had easy hands, to arrange the experiment; I have often in this way assisted him as his auditor. Already in the former century there was a general thought that there was a great conformity, and perhaps identity, between the electrical and magnetical force; it was only the question how to demonstrate it by experiments. Oersted tried to place the wire of his galvanic battery perpendicular (at right angles) over the magnetic needle, but remarked no sensible motion. Once, after the end of his lecture, as he had used a strong galvanic battery to other experiments, he said, "Let us now once, as the battery is in activity, try to place the wire parallel with the needle'; as this was made, he was quite struck with perplexity by seeing the needle making a great oscillation (almost at right angles with the magnetic meridian). Then he said,

The Hare and the Tortoise

"Let us now invert the direction of the current," and the needle deviated in the contrary direction. Thus the great detection was made; and it has been said, not without reason, that "he tumbled over it by accident". He had not before any more idea than any other person that the force should be *transversal*. But as Lagrange has said of Newton in a similar occasion, "such accidents only meet persons who deserve them".'

With kindling eyes, we learn, Oersted searched the faces around him, pointed to the apparatus with trembling hands, and invited his students to make the experiment for themselves. An account of his discovery, written in Latin, was printed in July 1820, and copies were sent to prominent persons at home and abroad. The first intimation Davy received however, was from Thomson's *Annals of Philosophy* on October 1st. That very morning he hurried to the Royal Institution and set to work with Michael to verify the facts and to make new investigations. There was indeed need for haste, for within two months Ampère in Paris was already publishing brilliant extensions of Oersted's discovery.

Davy himself did not make much progress. His powers were waning, and he still regarded Michael as a mere robot whose function was to follow his instructions mechanically, not to furnish original ideas. He did succeed, independently of Ampère, in magnetizing needles by the electric current, and he showed that a copper wire carrying a current could attract iron filings. He was probably not too pleased when his old friend Wollaston came along to the Royal Institution one day in April 1821 with a bright new notion—that a wire through which a current was passing would twist around upon its own axis when one pole of a magnet approached it—and asked for facilities to test it out forthwith. Faraday was not in the room when the experiment was performed and did not witness its failure—it would have succeeded if more delicate apparatus had been employed, as Ampère and Gore showed later—but he entered afterwards while Davy and Wollaston were still discussing it. Presumably he was not so interested as he ought to have been in their conversation and he offered only one 'hasty and useless' suggestion regarding some further

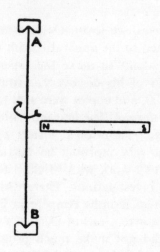

Wollaston's Experiment

(A wire AB, carrying an electric current, is in loose contact with two metal cups, A and B. The approach of a magnet was expected to cause the wire to rotate on its axis, as indicated by the circular arrow. This expectation was not fulfilled.)

efforts to make the wire roll on a board as the magnet was brought up to it, since he had other matters on his mind. Believe it or not, our young philosopher had fallen in love, and we must now interrupt our scientific narrative to get up-to-date with his private life since his return from the Continent.

The Hare and the Tortoise

It will be recalled that he had written to Abbott in 1813 a long series of letters on the art of lecturing. In January 1816, Abbott suggested that this topic should be resumed, but Michael replied that he was about to proceed from theory into practice. In point of fact, he delivered seven lectures on chemical subjects to his comrades at the City Philosophical Society during that year. Bence Jones reproduces long extracts from them which exhibit the love of accuracy and the cautious approach to questions of conjecture characteristic of his later career.

His increasing responsibilities necessitated steady curtailment of his communications with Abbott, a matter of deep regret to both. On 9th February 1816, Michael wrote to his friend: 'It is now 9 o'clock p.m., and I have just left the laboratory and the preparation for to-morrow's two lectures. Our double course makes me work enough, and to them add the attendance required by Sir Humphry in his researches; and then, if you compare my time with what is to be done in it, you will excuse the slow progress of our correspondence on my side. Understand me: I am not complaining; the more I have to do the more I learn.' Subsequently in the same year he remarked: 'When Mr. Brande left London in August, he gave the "Quarterly Journal" in charge to me: it has had very much of my time and care. It has, however, also been the means of giving me earlier information on some new objects of science.' Mr. Brande's recognition of the value of Michael's services was evidenced by a further increase in his salary to £100 a year; Michael must have felt that he also was 'on velvet' and could venture to be less spartan in his dining habits while increasing his aid to his mother.

In 1817 he gave another set of lectures to the City Philosophical Society; one of them, *Some Observations on the Means of obtaining Knowledge*, attained the dignity of print.

The Hare and the Tortoise

That summer, he spent a month's holiday with Huxtable in the West Country, and Huxtable noted: 'At the Narracote sheep-shearing, Mr. Faraday took part in the conviviality of the evening with much interest and good-humour.' Michael himself wrote to his mother from Barnstaple: 'I have been at sheep-shearing, merry-making, junketings, etc., and was never more merry; and I must say of the country people (of Devonshire, at least) that they are the most hospitable I could imagine. I have seen all your processes of thrashing, winnowing, cheese- and butter-making, and think I could even now give *you* some instructions.' In November he informed Abbott: 'In consequence of an arrangement I have made with a gentleman recommended to me by Sir H. Davy, I am engaged to give him lessons in mineralogy and chemistry thrice a week in the evening, for a few months.' More pocket-money!

In 1818 his letters to Abbott practically ceased, but not his friendship. Bence Jones remarks: 'As long as Abbott stayed in London, the friends met from time to time; and in after years, when he chanced to be in town, his greatest pleasure was to witness the success of Faraday in the theatre of the Royal Institution.' When Benjamin Abbott was an old man, he loved to relate how Michael carried out chemical experiments in the kitchen of his house, and how he rehearsed his first lecture standing behind that kitchen table. A third series of lectures that Michael now presented before the City Philosophical Society demonstrated his steady improvement in technique; so eager was he to perfect his delivery that he took a course of lessons from an elocutionist, B. H. Smart, paying half a guinea for each lesson. His bound notes on this elocution course fill 133 manuscript pages.

In 1819 he made a walking tour through Wales, visiting the copper works of Swansea, the mines of Anglesey, and the

The Hare and the Tortoise

slate mines of Bangor. His Journal records the pleasure he felt in ascending Cader Idris during a magnificent thunderstorm, but one minor interlude demands quotation in full, since it reveals so vividly his happy simplicity. The date is Tuesday, July 20th: 'After dinner I set off on a ramble to Melincourt, a waterfall on the north side of the valley, and about six miles from our inn. Here I got a little damsel for my guide who could not speak a word of English. We, however, talked together all the way to the fall, though neither knew what the other said. I was delighted with her burst of pleasure as, on turning a corner, she first showed me the waterfall. Whilst I was admiring the scene, my little Welsh damsel was busy running about, even under the stream, gathering strawberries. On returning from the fall I gave her a shilling that I might enjoy her pleasure: she curtsied, and I perceived her delight. She again ran before me back to the village, but wished to step aside every now and then to pull strawberries. Every bramble she carefully moved out of the way, and ventured her bare feet to try stony paths, that she might find the safest for mine. I observed her as she ran before me, when she met a village companion, open her hand to show her prize, but without any stoppage, word or other motion. When we returned to the village I bade her good-night, and she bade me farewell, both by her actions and I have no doubt her language too.'

On his return to London, a rather more mature damsel caught his fancy. One of the elders of the little Sandemanian congregation that gathered each Sunday at Paul's Alley, Red Cross Street, was Mr. Barnard, a silversmith of Paternoster Row. Mr. Barnard had two sons, Edward and George, and three daughters, the second of whom, Sarah, was twenty-one years of age. Michael became friendly with the whole family, and was incautious enough to show Edward a 'Common-

The Hare and the Tortoise

place book' in which he had copied all kinds of casual notes during the preceding five years. The book included not only the poem Michael had written against Love which forms the heading to this chapter, but also the following cynical aphorism:

'What is Love?—A nuisance to everybody but the parties concerned. A private affair which everyone but those concerned wishes to make public.'

Mischievous Edward blabbed about what he had read to his sister Sarah, between whom and Michael a romance seemed to be budding. On Michael's next visit, Sarah reproached him for his monstrous sentiments, and insisted on seeing the volume herself. Poor Michael sent it to her the next day, October 11th, with an abject appeal for mercy:

> *You ask'd me last night for the lines which I penn'd,*
> *When, exulting in ignorance, tempted by pride,*
> *I dared torpid hearts and cold breasts to commend,*
> *And affection's kind pow'r and soft joys to deride.*
>
> *If you urge it I cannot refuse your request:*
> *Though to grant it will punish severely my crime:*
> *But my fault I repent, and my errors detest;*
> *And I hoped to have shown my conversion in time.*
>
> *Remember, our laws in their mercy decide*
> *That no culprit be forced to give proof of his deed:*
> *They protect him though fall'n, his failings they hide,*
> *And enable the wretch from his crimes to recede.*
>
> *The principle's noble! I need not urge long*
> *Its adoption; then turn from a judge to a friend.*
> *Do not ask for the proof that I once acted wrong,*
> *But direct me and guide me the way to amend.*

The Hare and the Tortoise

The offended lady took an unconscionably long time to forgive him, however, since we find Michael nine long months later still racked with remorse. On 5th July 1820, he wrote to Sarah: 'You know my former prejudices, and my present thoughts—you know my weaknesses, my vanity, my whole mind; you have converted me from one erroneous way, let me hope you will attempt to correct what others are wrong. Do not injure me by withdrawing your friendship, or punish me for aiming to be more than a friend by making me less; and if you cannot grant me more, leave me what I possess, but hear me.'

Sarah dutifully showed this letter to her father and asked his advice. Father merely made matters worse by remarking that love turned philosophers into fools, thus landing himself in the same pretty pickle. His distracted daughter left London for Ramsgate with her married sister, Mrs. Reid, to postpone an immediate decision, but Michael pursued her thither before July was out, determined to run all risks of an unkind reception. He almost ruined his chances on the first evening, when he expressed strong disappointment at the place, and criticized all around him with a malicious tone, but he saw his danger, stopped just in time, and changed the subject to 'home and friends'. Two days afterwards he was still on tenterhooks: 'During a walk the conversation gradually became to me of the most pensive cast, and my mind was filled with melancholy thoughts. We went into a mill and got the miller to show us the machinery: thus seeking mechanical means of changing the subject, which, I fear, weighed heavy on both of us. But still our walk continued to have a very sombre, grave cast with it; and when I sat down in the chair at home, I wished for a moment that memory and sensation would leave me, and that I could pass away into nothing.'

The sky began to brighten when he took Sarah on an excursion to Dover and showed her the white outline of the French coast from Shakespeare's Cliff. He recorded in his Journal: 'I can never forget this day. Though I had ventured to plan it, I had had little hope of succeeding. But when the day came, from the first waking moment in it to the last it was full of interest to me: every circumstance bore so strongly on my hopes and fears that I seemed to live with thrice the energy I had ever done before.' And after a drive to Manston on the last evening of his stay he wrote: 'I could not have imagined a ride so pleasant as the one of this evening. The time of day, the scenery we passed through, and the places we visited, were all calm and composed, and heightened the feelings of tranquil enjoyment and perfect confidence which floated round our hearts. Not a moment's alloy of this evening's happiness occurred: everything was delightful to the last instant of my stay with my companion, because she was so.'

Matters now advanced slowly but surely—so typical of Faraday, so different from Davy—towards a happy ending. Here are a few extracts from some of Michael's love-letters to Sarah in the interval before their marriage.

'What can I call myself to convey most perfectly my affection and love to you? Can I, or can truth, say more than for this world I am yours?'

'I want to say a thousand kind and, believe me, heartfelt things to you, but am not master of words fit for the purpose; and still, as I ponder and think on you, chlorides, trials, oil, Davy, steel, miscellanea, mercury, and fifty other professional fancies swim before me and drive me further and further into the quandary of stupidness.'

'I tied up the enclosed key with my books last night, and make haste to return it lest its absence should occasion confusion. If it has, it will perhaps remind you of the disorder I

The Hare and the Tortoise

must be in here also for the want of a key—I mean the one to my heart. However, I know where my key is, and hope soon to have it here, and then the Institution will be all right again.'

In March 1821, indeed, Sir Humphry (impatient, no doubt, to lead his love-sick assistant back to normal) used his influence with the managers to obtain permission for Michael to bring his bride to live at the Royal Institution after their marriage, and secured his promotion in May to the position of 'superintendent of the house and laboratory'. His salary, however, remained at £100 a year. The question he had to face was, 'Could two live as cheaply as one?'

Anyway, the wedding took place on June 12th. Simple Michael, desiring that the day should be 'just like any other day', offended some of his near relations by not asking them to attend. In a letter to Mrs. Reid he wrote: 'There will be no bustle, no noise, no hurry occasioned even in one day's proceeding. In externals, that day will pass like all others, for it is in the heart that we expect and look for pleasure.'

Quiet wedding though it was, its memory remained fresh in Michael's thoughts for ever. In his diploma-book, where he carefully preserved all the certificates, awards and honours bestowed upon him by universities and scientific academies over the whole world,[1] he wrote in 1847: 'Amongst these records and events, I here insert the date of one which, as a source of honour and happiness, far exceeds the rest. We were *married* on June 12, 1821.' And two years later he recorded in his autobiographical notes: 'On June 12, 1821, he married—an event which more than any other contributed to his earthly happiness and healthful state of mind. The

---

[1] These distinctions totalled 97 at the time of his death. The celebrated electrician Riess, of Berlin, once addressed a long letter to him as follows: 'Professor Michael Faraday, Member of *all* Academies of Science, London.'

union has continued for twenty-eight years, and has nowise changed, except in depth and strength of its character.' Tyndall, his close associate in his declining years, has stated: 'In his relations to his wife he added *chivalry* to affection. Never, I believe, existed a manlier, purer, steadier love. Like a burning diamond, it continued to shed, for six and forty years, its white and smokeless glow.'

Certainly the most cherished of all the letters of congratulation he received on his marriage would be one from his supreme hero, Sir Humphry Davy. Humphry, who had married in haste and repented at leisure, concluded his note as follows: 'I hope you will continue quite well, and do much during the summer; and I wish you in your new state all that happiness which I am sure you deserve. I am, my dear Mr. Faraday, your sincere friend, H. Davy.'

Michael did indeed 'do much during the summer', but what he did had altogether unforeseen consequences.

CHAPTER SIX

The Superior Feelings of
Philosophic Men. I

The greatest of all my great advantages is that I had a model to
teach me what to avoid.

MICHAEL FARADAY

When Michael made this private remark to his intimate friend Tyndall in later life, he was referring—prepare yourself for a surprise—to Sir Humphry Davy. Do not surrender to your first flush of indignation and accuse him of arrant ingratitude; the following pages will furnish ample justification for Michael's right-about-turn from blind adoration to frank disapproval. And, after all, his personal grievances did not modify in the slightest degree his veneration for Humphry's scientific genius. He himself stated in 1835: 'Whenever I have ventured to follow in the path which Sir Humphry Davy has trod, I have done so with respect and with the highest admiration of his talents.' An extract from Thorpe's biography of Davy is also apposite: 'To the end of his days Faraday regarded Davy as his true master, preserving to the last, in spite of his knowledge of the moral frailties of Davy's nature, the respect and even deference which is to be seen in his early lecture notes and in his letters to his friend Abbott.'

This necessary introduction over, we may proceed with the

story of the next three years of Michael's life, which include three separate occasions when Humphry let him down badly. Humphry's part in these unfortunate episodes will be described as briefly as possible for two reasons. First of all, certain aspects of them have been discussed in detail already in *Humphry Davy: 'Pilot' of Penzance*; the continuity of the narrative demands some repetition here, but that repetition has been deliberately cut down to a minimum. Secondly, Michael himself would deprecate any escapable emphasis on his master's injustice towards him. His friend Lady Pollock relates: 'On one occasion, when some allusion to his early life brought on the mention of a painful passage between himself and Sir Humphry Davy, he rose abruptly from his seat and said: "Talk of something else, and never let me speak of this again, I wish to remember nothing but Davy's kindness." ' Nevertheless, historical truth requires that the essential facts should be clearly and fully depicted.

During the entire summer of 1821—there is no mention of any honeymoon—Michael was engaged in writing a comprehensive review of the new field of science, electromagnetism, for the *Annals of Philosophy* at the request of the editor of that journal, his old friend Phillips. He read through all the available papers on the subject, repeated most of the experiments described in them, and tried out new experiments himself. He could not realize Wollaston's expectation of the twisting of a wire round its axis (page 66), but on September 3rd he was successful in detecting something vastly more important—the revolution of a wire carrying an electric current round the pole of a magnet. When the wire first began to move, he also danced around the rotating circuit, his face radiant with joy, shouting: 'There they go! there they go! we've succeeded at last!' He then proposed to his young brother-in-law, George Barnard, who was watching him at his work, that they should celebrate by going to the theatre. 'Which shall it be?' 'Oh, let it be Astley's, to see the horses.' So to the circus they went—we hope with Sarah's permission —to watch the horses go round and round, but at the pit entrance there was a crush, a big fellow jostled little George, and Michael ordered him to behave himself and offered to fight him if he refused.

That is what Gladstone (who knew Faraday) tells us, and it is presumably correct, but no indication of excitement is to be found in Michael's laboratory notes. His record of September 3rd concludes: 'Very satisfactory, but make more sensible apparatus,' and September 4th begins with a rough diagram of this more sensible [sensitive?] apparatus, reproduced overleaf exactly as he drew it. It is well worth examination, for it represents the first electric motor. Many years will elapse before any practical application is made of this discovery, but the fundamental device on which all later developments depended is already there.

A deep basin with a bit of wax at the bottom is filled with mercury. A magnet is stuck upright in the wax so that its north pole is near the surface of the mercury. A piece of wire, with a small cork attached to float it just clear of the magnet, dips into the mercury; its upper end fits into a little inverted silver cup containing a globule of mercury. A second piece of wire is hooked over the side of the basin, and the two wires (marked Z and C respectively) are connected with the zinc and copper poles of a battery, completing an electric circuit. Immediately the wire Z starts to revolve round and round the magnet; if the magnet is reversed, the wire revolves round the south pole in the opposite direction; if the poles of the battery are transposed, reversal also occurs.

Using a slightly different set-up—the magnet floating vertically in mercury with one pole just above the surface and the other loaded with platinum to sink it—Michael also succeeded on September 4th in making the magnet circle round the

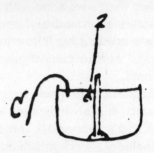

The first Electric Motor

(Faraday's original sketch)

central wire. He could *not*, however, manage to induce either the wire or the magnet to twist *on its own axis*, as Wollaston had attempted to do.

On September 12th, Michael sent De La Rive—who, far from being offended by the criticism of his theory of 'singing tubes' (p. 62), had invited him to correspond with him regularly on 'topics which occur in the general progress of science' —a summary of an article he had prepared for the *Quarterly Journal of Science* describing his discovery. He mentioned incidentally that Davy was out of town. Before Michael himself left London on a short holiday he tried to see Wollaston, to ask permission to refer to his views and experiments in this article, but Wollaston unfortunately was also out of town and the paper was published without any allusion to Wollaston's opinions. During Michael's country vacation he attained his thirtieth birthday, and we may imagine him and Sarah talking together about the praise that awaited him on his return to London.

The Superior Feelings of Philosophic Men. I

To his horror, he heard instead that rumours were rife 'affecting his honour and honesty', he was accused of being a thief and of having stolen Wollaston's idea. He wrote immediately to Stodart, his co-worker on steel alloys:

'If I understand aright, I am charged, (1) with not acknowledging the information I received in assisting Sir H. Davy in his experiments on this subject; (2) with concealing the theory and views of Dr. Wollaston; (3) with taking the subject whilst Dr. Wollaston was at work on it; and (4) with dishonourably taking Dr. Wollaston's thoughts, and pursuing them, without acknowledgment, to the results I have brought out.

'I want you to procure me an interview with Dr. Wollaston on his return to town; and I wish for this not only to apologize to him if I have unintentionally done him wrong, but to justify myself from the suspicions that are wrongly raised against me. Dr. Wollaston is so very far above me that even if he does feel himself wronged, he may not think it is of any importance, and I am but a young man, and without a name, and it probably does not matter much to science what becomes of me; but if by any circumstances I am subjected to unjust suspicions, it becomes no one more than him who may be said to preside over the equity of science, to assist in liberating me from them.'

Wollaston (a man of placid temperament) evidently did *not* attach much importance to the matter, since he made no response at all until Michael wrote to him directly: 'If I have done anyone wrong, it was quite unintentional, and the charge of behaving dishonourably is not true. I am bold enough, Sir, to beg the favour of a few minutes' conversation with you on this subject, simply for these reasons—that I can clear myself—that I owe obligations to you—that I respect you—that I am anxious to escape from unfounded impressions against me—and if I have done any wrong that I may apologize for it.'

Even now Wollaston did not realize how vital it was for him to bestir himself in rebutting the imputations against Faraday, for he merely replied: 'You seem to me to labour under some misapprehension of the strength of my feelings upon the subject to which you allude. As to the opinions which others may have of your conduct, that is your concern, not mine; and if you fully acquit yourself of making any incorrect use of the suggestions of others, it seems to me that you have no occasion to concern yourself much about the matter. But if you are desirous of any conversation with me, and could with convenience call to-morrow morning, between ten o'clock and half-past ten, you will be sure to find me.'

No record exists as to what ensued at this meeting, but Wollaston was obviously entirely satisfied, and showed that he harboured no trace of ill feeling towards Michael by coming to the Royal Institution several times to witness his experiments. When this became known publicly, the charges against Michael appeared to die away.

Meantime, what had Sir Humphry been doing in Michael's defence? So far as is known, he did not lift a finger. The suspicion has even been voiced that he was active in spreading the rumours of Michael's dishonesty; no grounds exist to warrant that suspicion now, but his later actions suggest that it might have some basis. Certainly he did not, as duty demanded, openly express his absolute trust in his assistant's integrity; presumably this inactivity was due to two factors. Wollaston was a very influential man both at the Royal Institution and in London society, and Humphry preferred to sit on the fence rather than run any risk of antagonizing him.

The Superior Feelings of Philosophic Men. I

A still stronger reason was his resentment over Michael's spectacular achievement in a field in which he himself had been working with only minor results. He always hated competition with his own investigations, and what right had Michael, of all people, to anticipate him in a scientific discovery? Let him keep to his proper sphere of doing just what he was told to do, and not get into further mischief.

Michael must have felt that he was in disfavour and, with a heavy heart, turned to less controversial and less attractive topics. Before doing so, however, he could not resist completing one experiment he had under way, and on Christmas morning he called Sarah down to his laboratory to see a novel phenomenon—a wire carrying an electric current revolving under the influence of the earth's magnetism alone. His laboratory notes for December 25th are appended *verbatim*, and his own rough sketch of the apparatus he employed is also shown overleaf.

'Rotation of a wire by the earth magnetism. In a large glass basin put mercury and a little nitric acid. Took about 6 inches of wire $\frac{1}{56}$ of inch thick, amalgamated it, formed a hook at top by which it was suspended from another fixed hook as in tube apparatus, put a little bit of cork on the lower end, the wire passing through it, and then held it over and on the mercury so that the wire formed an angle greater than the dip of the needle. Then connecting the mercury with one pole and the wire with the other it began to rotate and continued rotating whilst the connection continued. On changing the connection the direction of the motion changed also.'

We may visualize Sarah admiring this strange plaything of her husband with much bewilderment, thinking to herself: 'What a child he is, to be sure!', and then saying: 'Oh, Michael! aren't you wonderful? Don't you think I ought to go up now and cook the dinner?' Michael's felicity would be dimmed, however, by the recollection of that Christmas nine years ago, when he first heard from Sir Humphry. Wollaston might come and applaud his new invention, but Humphry, whom he valued above everybody else in the world, save Sarah, would not approve it. His god was beginning to totter; his faith in him was flickering.

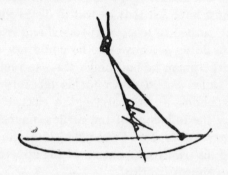

A Wire revolving under the Earth's Magnetism
(Faraday's Original sketch)

CHAPTER SEVEN

The Superior Feelings of Philosophic Men. II

When I discovered that neither I nor Sir Humphry Davy had the merit of first condensing the gases, and especially chlorine, I hastened to perform what I thought right, and had great pleasure in spontaneously doing honour to those who deserved it. Upon Mr. Northmore's complaint ten years after, that great injustice had been done to him, I was able to convince him that *I at least* had endeavoured to do him right.

MICHAEL FARADAY (1836)

During the whole of the following year, Michael did his best to behave like a good boy, and his conduct gave Sir Humphry no cause for complaint. At first, almost all the time left free for him for research was devoted to the completion of his work with Stodart on the improvement of steel alloys (page 63). One report on their joint results had already appeared in the *Quarterly Journal of Science* in 1820, a more comprehensive article was published in the *Philosophical Transactions* in March 1822.

The object of the investigation was to ascertain whether alloys could be devised superior to pure steel in cutting power and in resistance to rust. Preliminary work indicated that truly surprising changes in the quality of steel were induced by the addition of very minute quantities of other metals. Silver and the platinum metals seemed to show the

83

most promising effects, and Wollaston's liberality in furnishing scarce and valuable supplies of these metals in quantity sufficient to repeat the original laboratory tests on a large scale in a steel furnace at Sheffield was gratefully acknowledged.

Unfortunately the practical applications of the results were disappointing. 'Silver alloy'—steel to which 1 part in 500 of silver had been added—was the only alloy that interested the manufacturers; a Sheffield firm used it for some time in hearth fenders. The sole reward Michael himself received for his toil was a case of razors made from this alloy, and occasionally in later life he would give one of them to a friend as a special present. To De La Rive he wrote a number of letters detailing his various trials; one letter concludes: 'Pray pity us that, after two years' experiments, we have got no further; but I am sure, if you knew the labour of the experiments, you would applaud us for our perseverance at least.'

We ourselves can commiserate with Michael and his collaborator that their work on 'chromium alloy' was not followed up in a big way, since on the eve of the Faraday Centenary Celebrations in 1931 the famous metallurgist, Sir Robert Hadfield, analyzed some of their samples stored in the basement of the Royal Institution and proved that they had been the first to prepare what is now known as 'stainless steel'. The damasked surface of this alloy, when tempered by heating, is specifically noted by Stodart and Faraday; they even remark 'the blade of a sabre treated in this way would assuredly be beautiful, whatever its other properties might be; for of the value of the chrome alloy for edge-tools we are not prepared to speak'. What an opportunity British manufacturers missed!

That summer, also, Michael made a discovery that was by

no means original, namely that two could *not* live as cheaply as one. It was necessary for him to supplement his meagre income by undertaking consulting work, and here his friend Phillips—now a prominent man in his profession, already a Fellow of the Royal Society—proved most helpful. In July, Michael took Sarah and her mother to Ramsgate, and then went back to London before travelling to Swansea with Phillips to test out a new process in Vivian's copper works. The state of his finances may be gathered from an extract from a letter written to Sarah just before he left for Wales: 'Mr. Lawrence called in, and behaved with his usual generosity. He had called in the early part of the week, and, finding that I should be at the Institution on Saturday only, came up, as I have already said, and insisted on my accepting two ten-pound bank-notes for the information he professed to have obtained from me at various times. Is not this handsome? The money, as you know, could not have been at any time more acceptable.' The letter continues: 'And now, my dear girl, I must set business aside. I am tired of the dull detail of things, and want to talk of love to you.' Talk of love indeed he does, at great length, but we shall respect his privacy here. His devotion to Sarah, though, was evidently well-known to Mrs. Phillips, since she asked her husband on this self-same trip to borrow a copy of one of Michael's letters for his own improvement.

Back again in London, life flowed calmly on for Michael until March 1823, when two separate misunderstandings with Humphry began to trouble the waters, developing by degrees into veritable tempests. Only the first, which was the less violent, will be discussed in this chapter. Michael himself, thirteen years later, outlined its origin:

'In the spring of 1823, Mr. Brande was Professor of Chemistry, Sir Humphry Davy Honorary Professor of Chemistry, and I Chemical Assistant, in the Royal Institution. Having to give personal attendance on both the morning and afternoon chemical lectures, my time was very fully occupied. Whenever any circumstances relieved me in part from the duties of my situation, I used to select a subject of research, and try my skill upon it. Chlorine was with me a favourite object, and having before succeeded in discovering new compounds of that element with carbon, I had considered that body more deeply, and resolved to resume its consideration at the first opportunity: accordingly, the absence of Sir Humphry Davy from town having relieved me from a part of the laboratory duty, I took advantage of the leisure and the cold weather and worked upon frozen chlorine. On Sir Humphry Davy's return to town, he inquired what I had been doing, and I communicated the results to him as far as I had proceeded, and said I intended to publish them in the "Quarterly Journal of Science". It was then that he suggested to me the heating of the crystals in a closed tube. I did not at that time know what to anticipate, for Sir Humphry Davy *had not told me his expectations*, perhaps he left me unacquainted with them to try my ability.'

It is necessary to interpolate at this point that Michael is using an inaccurate expression when he states that he worked with 'frozen chlorine'; the substance he actually investigated was 'chlorine hydrate'. The first paragraph of his paper in the *Quarterly*, however, demonstrates that he knew this quite well: 'It was generally considered before the year 1810, that chlorine gas was condensible by cold into a solid state; and we were first instructed by Sir Humphry Davy, in his admirable researches into the nature of that substance, published in the "Philosophical Transactions" for 1810–11, that the solid body, obtained by cooling chlorine gas, was a compound with water; and that the dry gas could not be condensed at a temperature equal even to —40° Fahr., whilst on the contrary, moist gas, or a solution of chlorine in water, crystallised at the temperature of 40° Fahr.' Michael's paper consists essentially, in fact, of an analysis of chlorine hydrate; he finds that it contains 10 proportions of water to 1 of chlorine. The correct figure is 8 to 1 (Michael notes that it is possible that his proportion of chlorine is understated) but that is neither here nor there. Let us continue our story with an extract from *The Life of Sir Humphry Davy*, by Dr. Paris. Dr. Paris himself is speaking:

'I had been invited to dine with Sir Humphry Davy, on Wednesday the 5th of March 1823. On quitting my house for that purpose, I perceived that I had time to spare, and I accordingly called in my way at the Royal Institution. Upon descending into the laboratory I found Mr. Faraday engaged in experiments on chlorine and its hydrate in closed tubes. It appeared to me that the tube in which he was operating upon this substance contained some oily matter, and I rallied him upon the carelessness of employing soiled vessels. Mr. Faraday, upon inspecting the tube, acknowledged the justness of my remark, and expressed his surprise at the circumstance. In consequence of which, he immediately proceeded to file off the sealed end; when, to our great astonishment, the contents suddenly exploded, and the oily matter vanished!

'Mr. Faraday was completely at a loss to explain the occurrence, and proceeded to repeat the experiment with a view to its elucidation. I was unable, however, to remain and witness the result.

'Upon mentioning the circumstance to Sir Humphry Davy after dinner, he appeared much surprised; and after a few moments of apparent abstraction, he said, "I shall enquire about this experiment to-morrow".

'Early on the next morning, I received from Mr. Faraday

the following laconic note: Dear Sir, the *oil* you noticed yesterday turns out to be liquid chlorine. Yours faithfully, M. Faraday.'

Humphry's 'few moments of apparent abstraction', however, had potent consequences. Never did man's mind work as rapidly as his, he recognized immediately not only that Michael had been successful in liquefying chlorine, but also that he had discovered a general method of liquefying other refractory gases. As Paris relates:

'On the morning [Thursday, March 6th] after Mr. Faraday had condensed chlorine, Sir Humphry Davy had no sooner witnessed the result, than he called for a strong glass tube, and, having placed in it a quantity of muriate of ammonia and suphuric acid, and then sealed the end, he caused them to act upon each other, and thus condensed the muriatic acid [hydrogen chloride], which was evolved, into a liquid.'

Only a week later, on March 13th, Michael read a paper *On Fluid Chlorine* to the Royal Society, with Sir Humphry sitting in the Presidential Chair. This paper had been previously, Michael tells us, 'according to a custom consequent upon our relative positions, submitted to Sir Humphry Davy, and he altered it as he thought fit.' Simple Michael proceeds: 'This practice was one of great kindness to me, for various grammatical mistakes and awkward expressions were from time to time thus removed.' On this occasion, however, Humphry went much further, for his alterations comprise a passage at the beginning of the paper accentuating his role in the initiation of the work, and a long note at the end in which he definitely claims that he had in mind, as one possibility, the production of liquid chlorine from the very start. 'And then', as Michael ruefully remarks, 'he makes the subject his own', continuing thus:

'This last result having been obtained, it evidently led to

other researches of the same kind. I have requested Mr. Faraday to pursue these experiments, and to extend them to all the gases which are of considerable density, or to any extent soluble in water; and I hope soon to be able to lay an account of his results, with some applications of them that I propose to make, before the Society.'

Michael obediently did what he, as chemical assistant, was 'requested' to do, and on April 10th was in a position to report the condensation of sulphur dioxide, hydrogen sulphide, carbon dioxide, chlorine dioxide, nitrous oxide (Davy's 'laughing gas'), cyanogen and ammonia. This paper was also, of course, submitted to Sir Humphry before publication, and its opening paragraph does not read as if it were wholly Michael's composition:

'I had the honour, a few weeks since, of submitting to the Royal Society a paper on the reduction of chlorine to the liquid state. An important note was added to the paper by the President, on the general application of the means used in this case to the reduction of other gaseous bodies to the liquid state; and in illustration of the process, the production of liquid muriatic acid [hydrogen chloride] was described. Sir Humphry Davy did me the honour to request I would continue the experiments, which I have done under his general direction.'

The risk involved in conducting the experiments, however, was entirely Michael's, and that risk was extreme. I can myself vouch directly for this, since when I delivered the Christmas Lectures at the Royal Institution in 1938 I demonstrated the production of liquid chlorine, using one of Michael's original tubes. The apparatus is shown in the annexed diagram; the chlorine hydrate crystals on the left were heated by a small Bunsen flame, and the slow condensation of an oily liquid in the ice-cooled end on the right was shown to the audience by casting its shadow on a screen with the help of a lantern. Thick sheets of plate glass, in front and behind, protected everyone from danger, but a minor mishap had occurred during a rehearsal and I heaved a deep sigh of relief when the experiment was safely concluded.

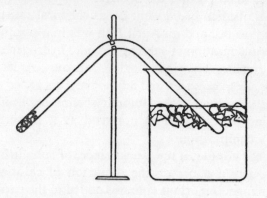

Liquefaction of chlorine

Michael's mishaps were not minor; he experienced many severe explosions. Here is a brief account of one in a letter to Huxtable on March 23rd: 'I met with another explosion on Saturday evening, which has again laid up my eyes. It was from one of my tubes, and was so powerful as to drive the pieces of glass like pistol-shot through a window. However, I am getting better, and expect to see as well as ever in a few days. My eyes were filled with glass at first.' How Michael must have been reminded of the good old days when Humphry and he were working together on nitrogen trichloride (page 35)! But then, reckless of peril, they marched into battle side by side; now Sir Humphry resembled the Duke of Plaza Toro—'he led his regiment from behind; he found it less exciting.'

The Superior Feelings of Philosophic Men. II

Still Michael was patient, and registered no protest; it was not until 1836 that some remarks made by Dr. John Davy in a biography of his dead brother drove him unwillingly into utterance. Dr. Davy wrote with regard to the condensation of gases: 'I am surprised that Mr. Faraday has not come forward to do him [Sir Humphry Davy] justice. As I view the matter, it appears hardly less necessary to his own honest fame than his acknowledgment to Dr. Wollaston, on the subject of the first idea of the rotatory magnetic motion.' And even then Michael contented himself with the calm reply:

'I have never remarked upon nor denied Sir H. Davy's right to his share of the condensation of chlorine or the other gases; on the contrary, I think that I long ago did him full "justice" in the papers themselves. How could it be otherwise? He saw and revised the manuscripts; through his hands they went to the Royal Society, of which he was President at the time; and he saw and revised the printer's proofs. Although he did not tell me of his expectations when he suggested the heating the crystals in a closed tube, yet I have no doubt that he had them; and though perhaps I regretted losing my subject, I was too much indebted to him for much previous kindness to think of saying that that was mine which he said was his. But *observe* (for my sake), that Sir H. Davy nowhere states that he told me what he expected, or contradicts the passages in the first paper of mine which describe my course of thought, and in which I claim the development of the actual results.'

Michael's friends were less tolerant at the time, they were indignant at Humphry's high-handed conduct. And what can we say here in Davy's defence? It is true that, strictly speaking, he was justified by the fact that it was then common practice to consider any idea developed by an assistant in a research laboratory as the property of his professor, but Faraday was far from being a mere assistant. How would Davy have felt if Dr. Beddoes, under whose nominal direction he was working when he discovered the anaesthetic properties of laughing gas at the Pneumatic Institution at Bristol in 1800, had claimed that discovery as his own? Surely he had gained sufficient glory for himself by now, and could afford to be generous!

Humphry, however, was always hungry for fame and could never tolerate a rival. He was in no mood to be benevolent; if this Man Friday of his threatened to usurp the role of Robinson Crusoe, then Man Friday must be taught a sharp lesson. The thunder of the more serious storm mentioned a few pages back, indeed, was already beginning to roll.

Before we leave this lesser one, however, there is an historical postscript to add. In 1824, after all the rumblings had died down, Michael published a paper in the *Quarterly Journal of Science* which begins as follows: 'I was not aware at the time when I first observed the liquefaction of chlorine gas, nor until very lately, that any of the class of bodies called *gases* had been reduced into fluid form; but having during the last few weeks sought for instances where such results might have been afforded without the knowledge of the experimenter, I was surprised to find several recorded cases. I have thought it right therefore to bring these cases together, and only justice to endeavour to secure for them a more general attention than they appear as yet to have gained.' The most remarkable of such experiments were some performed by Northmore on chlorine in the years 1805–6, and Michael quotes from Northmore's results to show that there can be no doubt that true liquefaction was then accomplished. Davy must have boiled with rage when this was brought to his notice, but he did not follow Faraday's example. He lay low and said nothing.

CHAPTER EIGHT

The Superior Feelings of Philosophic Men. III

In relation to Davy's opposition to my election at the Royal Society.

Sir H. Davy angry, May 30.
Phillips' report through Mr. Children, June 5.
Mr. Warburton called first time, June 5 (evening).
I called on Dr. Wollaston, and he not in town, June 9.
I called on Dr. Wollaston, and saw him, June 14.
I called at Sir H. Davy's, and he called on me, June 17.

MICHAEL FARADAY'S NOTES (1823)

O n the morning of 6th March 1823, Humphry saw Michael liquefy chlorine and himself liquefied hydrogen chloride. On the afternoon of 6th March 1823, Humphry read a communication to the Royal Society entitled *On a new Phenomenon of Electromagnetism.* Now what was electromagnetic in that article was not new, but merely another form of Faraday's rotations; and the *new phenomenon* was not only purely electrical, but had already been discovered by Ampère six months previously. Perhaps Humphry did not know this because he was also on bad terms now with his old friend Ampère. His address ended with the following most imprudent remark: 'I cannot with propriety conclude without mentioning a circumstance in the history of the progress of electro-magnetism, which, though well known to many Fellows of this Society, has, I believe, never been made public; namely, that we owe to the sagacity of Dr. Wollaston the first idea of the possibility of the rotation of the electro-magnetic wire round its axis by the approach of a magnet; and I witnessed, early in 1821, an unsuccessful experiment which he made to produce the effect.'

When this paper was reported upon in the *Annals of Philosophy* in April, the reporter confused the rotation of the wire on its own axis [Wollaston] with the rotation of the wire round a magnet [Faraday], and stated: 'Had not an experiment on the subject made by Dr. W. in the laboratory of the Royal Institution, and witnessed by Sir Humphry, failed *merely through an accident* which happened to the apparatus, *he would have been the discoverer of that phenomenon.'* Humphry himself, discussing this with Michael, declared that it was 'inaccurate and very unjust', and advised him to draw up a contradiction. Michael did so, and submitted his draft to Humphry for approval; Humphry amended it so that the contradiction was more definite and emphatic, and the May issue of the *Annals of Philosophy* duly admitted that its April report 'was unjust to Mr. Faraday and did not at all convey the sense of the author'.

So far, so good, but it is easier to start a libel than to stop it, and Michael found himself subjected to a great deal of annoyance by the resurrection of the old scandal (which was revived even as late as 1836; see page 91) that he had stolen Wollaston's original idea. His friends, of whom Phillips was the foremost, now felt that they must take some decisive step to make Michael's scientific reputation secure. They determined, in view of his outstanding achievements over the last few years, to nominate him for election as a Fellow of the Royal Society and, to make assurance doubly sure, they obtained Wollaston's consent to function as the first of the twenty-nine signatories to his certificate.

Now the fat was well and truly in the fire; Humphry was galvanized into action immediately. Taking off his gloves, he fought against Michael's election with might and main. It cannot be true, as one writer has suggested, that his disgruntlement sprang from the fact that he had not been asked to propose Michael, since as President of the Royal Society he was precluded from doing so. He could, and he should, have helped him materially by quiet commendation in private, but far from doing that he went around actively urging his conviction that Michael was an unfit candidate. One of Michael's proposers informed him that: 'Sir Humphry Davy had walked for an hour round the courtyard of Somerset House, arguing that Faraday ought not to be elected.' He even took the unprecedented action of attempting to coerce Michael into withdrawing his name. Here is the story as related by Michael himself: 'Sir H. Davy told me I must take down my certificate. I replied that I had not put it up; that I could not take it down, as it was put up by my proposers. He then said I must get my proposers to take it down. I answered that I knew they would not do so. Then he said, I as President will take it down. I replied that I was sure Sir H. Davy would do what he thought was for the good of the Royal Society.'

Knowing as we do Michael's natural tendency to quick resentment when exposed to indignity, we must admire his moderation in this interchange. However unjust his former benefactor's prejudices might be, he was resolved not to lose *his* temper. He did, nevertheless, find it necessary to take drastic measures to counteract the aspersions against his character that were now once more in circulation. 'I do not believe', says Michael in his simplicity, 'that anyone willingly was the cause of this state of things, but all seemed confusion, and generally to my disadvantage.' With the approval of Wollaston himself, he published on July 1st an historical statement respecting electromagnetic rotation that set out all the facts fairly. He had several interviews with Mr. Warburton, Wollaston's most intimate friend, who had evidently been primed against him and who made no secret of the fact that he intended, when Faraday's name came up for ballot, to take the opportunity of remarking in public on that part of Faraday's conduct to which he objected. On July 8th Warburton wrote to Michael that he would now tell all those to whom he had communicated this intention, *including the President himself*: 'My objections to you as a Fellow are and ought to be withdrawn; I now wish to forward your election.'

This was the turning-point in the struggle. Michael's profound relief is apparent in an excerpt from his reply: 'Two months ago I had made up my mind to be rejected by the Royal Society as a Fellow, notwithstanding the knowledge I had that many would do me justice; and, in the then state of my mind, rejection or reception would have been equally indifferent to me. Now that I have experienced so fully the kindness and liberality of Dr. Wollaston, which has been constant throughout the whole affair, and that I find an expression of good-will strong and general towards me, I am delighted by the hope I have of being honoured by Fellowship with the Society; and I thank you sincerely for your promise of support in my election, because I know you would not give it unless you sincerely thought me a fit person to be admitted.'

So Michael's certificate was *not* taken down and, after it had been suspended for the statutory ten meetings, a formal ballot was held on 8th January 1824. The voting was almost unanimous in his favour, only one black ball being recorded against him. Fortunately the election was secret, so that nobody knows whose hand dropped that black ball into the box.

In any case, Humphry now showed himself a good sport. In all fairness to him, it must be mentioned that he was a very sick man during this stormy period, and was much worried by domestic difficulties (Lady Davy certainly could not compete with Sarah as a helpmate); perhaps this may extenuate his conduct to some degree. When failing health forced him to resign from all connection with the Royal Institution early in 1825, he stated that he considered the talents and services of Mr. Faraday entitled him to some mark of approbation from the managers. These sentiments met with the cordial concurrence of the board, and on February 7th it was resolved 'that Mr. Faraday be appointed Director of the Laboratory under the superintendence of the Professor of Chemistry [Mr. Brande].' His salary, however, remained static at £100 a year!

Michael himself bore no resentment towards Humphry, although he sadly confessed that after his election as F.R.S. their relations were never the same as before. His idol had now collapsed completely. It was a melancholy conclusion to their long association, but let me round it off more happily by repeating a story told by Jean Baptiste Dumas (see page 44):

'Faraday never forgot what he owed to Davy. Visiting him at the family lunch, twenty years after the death of the latter, he noticed evidently that I responded with some coolness to the praises which the recollection of Davy's great discoveries had evoked from him. He made no comment. But, after the meal, he simply took me down to the library of the Royal Institution, and stopping before the portrait of Davy, he said: "He was a great man, wasn't he?" Then, turning round, he added, "It was here that he spoke to me for the first time."

I bowed. We went to the laboratory. Faraday took out a notebook, opened it and pointed out with his finger the words written by Davy, at the very moment when by means of the battery he had just decomposed potash, and had seen the first globule of potassium ever isolated by the hand of man. Davy had traced with a feverish hand a circle which separates them from the rest of the page: the words, "Capital Experiment," which he wrote below, cannot be read without emotion by any true chemist. I confessed myself conquered, and this time, without hesitating longer, I joined in the admiration of my good friend.'

CHAPTER NINE

The Great Sacrifice

Annual income twenty pounds, annual expenditure nineteen nineteen six, result happiness. Annual income twenty pounds, annual expenditure twenty pounds ought and six, result misery.

CHARLES DICKENS

Michael's loyalty and devotion were henceforth transferred from Davy to Davy's laboratory, the Royal Institution. During the next decade, this underwent acute financial troubles; Michael once told the managers bluntly: 'We are living on the parings of our own skin.' In 1823 a committee of investigation reported: 'The Committee are certainly of opinion that no reduction can be made in Mr. Faraday's salary—£100 per annum, house, coals, and candles; and beg to express their regret that the circumstances of the Institution are not such as to justify their proposing such an increase of it as the variety of duties which Mr. Faraday has to perform, and the zeal and ability with which he performs them, appear to merit.' In the following year, however, Mr. Fuller endowed a chair of chemistry at the Royal Institution, to which Michael was appointed for life. This brought his official income up to £200 a year, but it was not until 1853 that this sum was increased to £300. Nevertheless, attractive offers of positions elsewhere were firmly declined. In 1827, for example, he was asked to accept the professorship of chemistry in the newly established University of London; he replied: 'I think it a matter of duty and

The Great Sacrifice

gratitude on my part to do what I can for the good of the Royal Institution in the present attempt to establish it firmly. The Institution has been a source of knowledge and pleasure to me for the last fourteen years, and though it does not pay me in salary for what I *now* strive to do for it, yet I possess the kind feelings and good-will of its authorities and members, and all the privileges it can grant or I require; and, moreover, I remember the protection it has afforded me during the past years of my scientific life.' In 1844, when Davy's former patron, Hope, died after holding the chair of chemistry at the University of Edinburgh for nearly fifty years, Michael refused a much more lucrative invitation. It is just as well for the salmon and grouse of Scotland that Humphry, whose boyhood dream had been to obtain an Edinburgh degree, did not have this particular opportunity!

Man must live, however (and woman also, no doubt Sarah would have added); moreover, Michael still had his aged mother to support. The consulting work that Phillips had first obtained for him steadily grew with his steadily growing reputation, and in 1829 he saw his way clear to take on the duties of lecturer in chemistry at the Military Academy, Woolwich, for which he received £200 annually for twenty lectures. This post he held until 1849, when his friend Abel succeeded him. Abel remarked later: 'No man was so respected, admired, and beloved as a teacher at the Military Academy in former days as Faraday. Many are the little incidents which have been communicated to me by his pupils illustrative of his charms as a lecturer, and of his kindly feelings for the youths to whom he endeavoured to impart a taste for, if not a knowledge of, science.'

These extra responsibilities did not involve any contraction of his work at the Royal Institution. He had already delivered his first lecture there in 1823, when he was unexpectedly

The Great Sacrifice

called upon as a substitute for Brande, who had fallen ill; like Davy, he is reported to have 'acquitted himself admirably well'. In 1824 he took over half of Brande's lecture courses in chemistry and physics; in 1825 his first action as Director of the Laboratory was to invite the members of the Institution to attend evening demonstrations there; in 1826 he expanded such informal gatherings into regular Friday evening discourses, many of which he delivered himself. These Friday evening addresses by distinguished lecturers still play a prominent part in the activities of the Royal Institution, but no one has ever excelled Faraday in their presentation. Here is a picture by Lady Pollock: 'His was an irresistible eloquence, which compelled attention and insisted upon sympathy. It waked the young from their visions, and the old from their dreams. There was a gleaming in his eyes which no painter could copy, and which no poet could describe.' In 1826 also he inaugurated the Christmas Courses of Lectures 'adapted to a juvenile auditory', but these will be commented upon in greater detail later.

Neither did his output of original research, for some years, suffer any diminution. In 1825 he achieved what after-events converted into his greatest chemical discovery, the isolation of a new substance first called 'bicarbonate of hydrogen' but now better known as benzene. As was remarked when the centenary of this discovery was celebrated at an international gathering of organic chemists in London in 1925, it was destined to put millions of pounds (and marks, and dollars) into the pockets of manufacturers, to provide employment for millions of workers, and to place within the reach of everyone materials that had hitherto either been non-existent or obtainable only by the well-to-do. For benzene is the parent substance of all aromatic compounds, which constitute the basis of the great majority of modern dyes, perfumes and medicinal products. In later life Michael often enjoyed looking in at Hofmann's laboratory at the Royal College of Chemistry in South Kensington to witness the initial triumphs made there in those fields, and on 16th May 1861, he attended a meeting of the Chemical Society where a young man of twenty-three had been asked to deliver an address 'On Colouring Matters derived from Coal Tar'. That young man was William Henry Perkin, who five years previously had isolated mauve, the first aniline dye. The congratulations Michael extended to him at the end of his lecture must have lifted him to the seventh heaven of happiness.

When Michael first obtained benzene he did not, of course, realize its future importance. It was the one time in his life that he was handed a great discovery on a platter; all his other successes were won by the sweat of his brow. But, if he was lucky, he made admirable use of his luck. Sir William Pope summed up the situation at the Centenary Celebrations: 'The memoir in which Faraday describes the isolation of this hydrocarbon is written in very simple language, but it reveals throughout the handiwork of a genius in experimentation, and of an unrivalled master in the interpretation of experimental results.' What he actually did can be described very briefly.

Around 1820, gas began to come into wide use in Great Britain as a household illuminant; this gas was made by decomposing whale-oil at a red heat and stored in iron cylinders under high pressure. Michael secured from the Portable Gas Company considerable quantities of a fluid that separated out during the compression. He found this fluid to be a very complex mixture of substances, but by repeated distillation, collecting the products that came over at different temperatures in different receivers, he separated it into a series of fractions, ranging from limpid liquids to thick syrups. The

The Great Sacrifice

fractions boiling between 176° and 190° Fahrenheit appeared to be more uniform than the others, so Michael put them into a freezing mixture. Large amounts of a solid then deposited, and Michael purified this solid from the residual mother-liquor by means of a Bramah filter-press. Beautiful white crystals were obtained, which were redistilled from quicklime to remove traces of water. The final product, with a melting-point of 42° Fahrenheit, Michael analyzed with phenomenal ingenuity and accuracy; it was pure benzene, and he concluded his investigation by a thorough study of its physical and chemical properties. The leading continental chemist Berzelius, formerly Davy's bitter rival, called this research 'without doubt one of the most important which has enriched chemistry during 1825'; Sir William Pope comments that Michael's consummate art must have convinced the Swedish giant at once that a new epoch had dawned in organic chemistry.

It is highly probable that the 'gas-fluid problem' was first brought to Michael's notice by his elder brother Robert who, moving with the times, had changed his occupation from blacksmith to gas-fitter and lamp-maker. In spite of the difference in their stations, Robert and Michael maintained perfect family solidarity; Robert used to attend Michael's lectures as frequently as business allowed him. Frank Barnard, Sarah's younger brother, later a well-known artist, tells a characteristic story about this: 'One day Robert was sitting in the Royal Institution just previous to a lecture by the young and rising philosopher, when he heard a couple of gentlemen behind him descanting on the natural gifts and rapid rise of the lecturer. The brother—perhaps not fully apprehending the purport of their talk—listened with growing indignation while one of them dilated on the lowness of

Faraday's origin. "Why," said the speaker, "I believe he was a mere shoe-black at one time." Robert could endure this no longer; but turning sharply round he demanded: "Pray, sir, did he ever black your shoes?" "Oh! dear no, certainly not," replied the gentleman, much abashed.'

Michael also repaid Robert for past kindnesses by assisting him in his trade. When the Athenaeum Club was founded in 1823, Michael functioned as its first secretary. He soon found the duties of this position tiresome, and resigned in favour of his friend Magrath, but he remained on the House Committee. Complaint was made in 1839 by the members that they suffered from headaches through the fumes of the gas illumination employed, while the bindings of the books in the library were also seriously injured. Michael cured all this by an ingenious arrangement which carried off all the products of combustion without their ever mixing with the air of the room. This device could, of course, be applied generally—Michael invented it orginally to prevent the icing-up of the windows of lighthouses—but he wrote to Robert: 'And now, dear brother, believing this particular arrangement of the ventilating flue to be my own invention, and having no intention of turning it to any pecuniary use for myself, I am most happy to give freely all my rights in it over to you.' Sad to say, Robert did not live long to benefit from his younger brother's generosity. In 1846 he was killed in a street accident; a few lines from a letter written to Sarah, who was on holiday at Tunbridge Wells, betray Michael's distress: 'Dear Heart, My brother, exhausted by the results of the terrible accident which happened to him, died about seven o'clock. He was taken to University Hospital, where I saw his corpse this morning, and though sadly bruised, it was just my dear brother. Come home, dearest.'

The Great Sacrifice

In 1825, also, Michael began some arduous research work on optical glass, work that continued for five years. The Royal Society had appointed a committee to investigate the improvement of glass for optical purposes, and Michael was given the responsibility of the chemical part of the inquiry, including the small-scale manufacture of new types of glass. The preliminary experiments were conducted under great difficulties at the Falcon Glass Works, but in 1827 Michael obtained permission to equip a room at the Royal Institution with special furnaces and to engage an assistant. This assistant, Sergeant Anderson of the Royal Artillery, stayed on as Michael's devoted servant for nearly forty years. Note that Micahel did not select a young man to help him, possibly he feared the risk of future conflicts, with himself in the role of Davy. As Benjamin Abbott informs us, 'Sergeant Anderson was chosen simply because of the habits of strict obedience his military training had given him. His duty was to keep the furnaces always at the same heat, and the water in the ashpit always at the same level. In the evening he was released, but one night Faraday forgot to tell Anderson he could go home, and early next morning he found his faithful servant still stoking the glowing furnace, as he had been doing all night long.' And in a footnote to a paper published in 1845 Michael states: 'I cannot resist the occasion that is thus offered me of mentioning the name of Mr. Anderson, who came to me as an assistant in the glass experiments, and has remained ever since in the laboratory of the Royal Institution. He assisted me in all the researches into which I have entered since that time; and to his care, steadiness, exactitude, and faithfulness in the performance of all that has been committed to his charge, I am much indebted.'

This work on glass, though strongly supported by the Admiralty, resembled the research on steel alloys in leading to results of little immediate practical value. Common flint and crown glasses were first exhaustively studied, but after September 1828 efforts were confined to 'the preparation and perfection of peculiar heavy and fusible glasses'. Here considerable progress was made, and late in 1829 Michael was honoured by an invitation to present his results to the Royal Society in its annual Bakerian Lecture. In fact, he had so much to say that three sessions were occupied in its delivery.

Weighty though Michael's conclusions might be, he still could not persuade the manufacturers to undertake large-scale production of his new type of glass, and in 1830 he discontinued his experiments. Like those on steel alloys, however, they were not fruitless, since it was with the help of a bar made of one of his heavy glasses, containing borosilicate of lead, that he first succeeded in showing the effect of magnetism on light and the phenomenon of diamagnetism—two of his most momentous discoveries—fifteen years later.

All this long labour had been absolutely gratuitous. Meanwhile, how was the wolf being kept from the door? The answer to this question is that the wolf had retired baffled for the time being. Michael had published in 1827 a book on *Chemical Manipulation*, describing in minute detail all the operations of a laboratory; it was very successful; it went through three editions and was also reprinted in America. In 1838, he declined to issue a fourth edition, since he regarded it as out-of-date. Nevertheless, more than one professor of chemistry still recommends it to-day as an invaluable guide to students starting research. It is severely methodical, but a few sentences deserve quotation: 'Those who love the science will never think a damp kitchen or a small attic sufficient for their purpose. Dr. Marcet [the husband of Michael's first instructress, see page 26], when he purchased a house on the

The Great Sacrifice

banks of the lake of Geneva, appropriated one of the best rooms in it to the purposes of a laboratory, not knowing, as he himself said, why he should not do what he could to make that a pleasant place where he found so much pleasure.' On the other hand, discussing the essential furniture of a laboratory, Michael says firmly: 'One chair will be found quite sufficient, for a laboratory is no place for persons not engaged in the operations going on there.'

More important were the fees he obtained from consulting work. Phillips had put him into this line some years previously, now his own achievements made the demand for his services as analyst, as adviser to chemical firms, and as expert witness in the courts go up by leaps and bounds. How scrupulous he was, however, in accepting fees is shown by the following lines in a letter to Phillips: 'With regard to the five guineas, do not think of it for a moment. Whilst I supposed a mercantile concern wanted my opinion for its own interested uses, I saw no reason why it should not pay me; but it is altogether another matter when it becomes *your affair*. I do not think you would have wished *me* to pay *you* five guineas for anything you might have done personally for me. "Dog don't eat dog", as Sir E. Home said to me in a similar case. The affair is settled.' In spite of such punctiliousness, which must have amused Phillips greatly, his 'professional business', as he termed it, brought him in 1830 more than £1,000. In 1831 he was on the way to making a lot more and, according to Tyndall, he could easily have raised his business income by 1832 to £5,000 a year. The cost of living was low at that period, income tax had not yet been introduced, it is obvious that Michael might have died a very wealthy man.

He himself willed otherwise. Money meant nothing to him, except as a means for helping others; he and Sarah lived in a simple manner—comfortably but not luxuriously—and the whole of his surplus funds went in donations to the poor and in contributions to the general funds of his Church. Gladstone states: 'The porter of the Royal Institution has shown me, among his treasured memorials, a large number of forms for post-office orders, for sums varying from five shillings to five pounds, which Faraday was in the habit of sending in that way to different recipients of his thoughtful bounty.' All this was done, not ostentatiously, but in secret; Michael once warned a friend: 'I never let my name go to such acts, and very rarely even the initials of my name.'

The truth is that Michael was, through these years, a most unhappy man. He wanted above all else to continue his work on electricity and magnetism, but everything was conspiring to prevent him. First of all, it seemed inadvisable to rush into extensive publication while Davy was still active; that might precipitate more trouble. How peppery Humphry had become is seen by Michael's introductory sentence to a short paper in 1826 on the confinement of dry gases over mercury, describing some of the earliest work ever done on gaseous diffusion: 'The results of an experiment made June 26, 1823, by myself, and quoted as such, having been deemed of sufficient interest to be doubted, I have been induced to repeat it.' Michael is too tactful to mention it, but the doubter was Davy; the last entry in Humphry's handwriting in the laboratory book of the Royal Institution describes a vain attempt to confute Michael's conclusions.

In December 1826 Sir Humphry suffered a paralytic stroke; the following year he resigned the Presidency of the Royal Society; it was evident that his days were numbered. The ruin of what he was, he lingered on until May 1829, when at Geneva:

> *Came the blind Fury with th' abhorred shears*
> *And slit the thin-spun life.*

The Great Sacrifice

Wollaston had died a few months earlier; Michael was now quite free to go ahead, but he first had to finish his assignment on optical glass. This appeared to end in 1830, and he immediately resumed some very spasmodic efforts he had been making during the past seven years to develop new discoveries in electromagnetism. And now he found, to his dismay, that his 'business commitments' handicapped his progress intolerably.

Firm action had to be taken, and Michael took it. Anticipating Mr. Micawber's financial analysis quoted at the head of this chapter, he pursued the same line of thought and arrived at a diametrically opposite conclusion. 'Ye cannot serve Science and Mammon' was the operative phrase in his deliberations. He could be rich and miserable, or he could be poor and happy; he chose the latter.

This bold decision was expedited by a report made by the Committee for the Improvement in Optical Glass to the Council of the Royal Society in 1831. This report stated: 'The telescope made with Mr. Faraday's glass has been examined by Captain Kater and Mr. Pond. It bears as great a power as can reasonably be expected, and is very achromatic. The Committee therefore recommend that Mr. Faraday be requested to make a perfect piece of glass of the largest size that his present apparatus will admit, and also to teach some person to manufacture the glass for general sale.'

Michael's reply to Dr. Roget, Secretary of the Royal Society, ran as follows:

'Royal Institution; July 4, 1831.

'Dear Sir,

'I send you herewith four large and two small manuscript volumes relating to optical glass, and comprising the journal book and sub-committee book, since the period that experimental investigations commenced at the Royal Institution.

'With reference to the request which the Council of the Royal Society have done me the honour of making—namely, that I should continue the investigation—I should, under circumstances of perfect freedom, assent to it at once; but obliged as I have been to devote the whole of my spare time to the experiments already described, and consequently to resign the pursuit of such philosophical inquiries as suggested themselves to my own mind, I would wish, under present circumstances, to lay the glass aside for a while, that I may enjoy the pleasure of working out my own thoughts on other subjects.

'If at a future time the investigation should be renewed, I must beg it to be clearly understood, I cannot promise full success should I resume it: all that industry and my abilities can effect shall be done; but to perfect a manufacture, not being a manufacturer, is what I am not bold enough to promise.'

Note carefully the date at the top of this letter, for this was truly Michael's 'Independence Day'! Not only was he determined to free himself from the slavery of glass manufacture, but he also proposed to give up his professional practice completely in order to devote all his time to 'philosophical inquiries'. In point of fact, his external earnings in 1832 sank to £155, and in no subsequent year did they even approach this figure. From 1845 until his death in 1867, his business income was exactly zero.

What did Sarah say to all this? She may have had some forebodings—'Would that wolf return now? Would Michael have to deprive himself of dinner again?'—but Sarah had no Mayfair ambitions and what her man decided to do must be right. Unlike Lady Davy, Sarah always remained modestly in the background of her husband's life, but here is a charming compliment paid her in a letter to Michael from the famous German chemist Liebig after he had attended the British Association Meeting at York in 1844: 'Often do my thoughts wander back to the period which I spent in England, among the many pleasant hours of which the remembrance of those passed with you and your amiable wife is to me always the dearest and most agreeable. With the purest pleasure I bring to mind my walk with her, in the botanical garden at York, when I was afforded a glance of the richness of her mind; what a rare treasure you possess in her!'

Before we leave Liebig, some further statements from him call for brief examination. In 1837, Liebig had made an earlier visit to England and reported to his master Berzelius: 'England is not the home of science. The chemists are ashamed to call themselves chemists, because the apothecaries, who are despised, have appropriated the name.' Now my readers may have noticed that our Michael was not wont to call himself a chemist—nor after 1831, when he became primarily interested in physics, did he call himself a physicist —he preferred to style himself a philosopher. Was *he* ashamed of the name of chemist? Not a whit, he merely followed the example of his paragon Davy, and Davy patterned himself upon *his* hero, Joseph Black of Edinburgh. All three fully merited the broader title, which only modern usage has rendered archaic.

Liebig's disparaging opinion of British scientists did not, in any case, extend to Faraday, since in his discourse on *Induction and Deduction* he makes this remark: 'I have heard mathematical physicists deplore that Faraday's records of his labours were difficult to read and understand, that they often resembled rather abstracts from a diary. But the fault was

The Great Sacrifice

theirs, not Faraday's. To physicists who have approached physics by the road of chemistry, Faraday's memoirs sound like admirably beautiful music.'

And, finally, Liebig's understanding and approval of Michael's grand sacrifice is expressed in a third extract:

'What struck me most in England was the perception that only those works which have a practical tendency awake attention and command respect; while the purely scientific, which possess far greater merit, are almost unknown. And yet the latter are the proper and true source from which the others flow. Practice alone can never lead to the discovery of a truth or a principle. In Germany it is quite the contrary. Here, in the eyes of scientific men, no value, or at least but a trifling one, is placed on the practical results. The enrichment of science is alone considered worthy of attention. I do not mean to say that this is better; for both nations the *golden medium* would certainly be a real good fortune.'

Now it is time for me to recount the consequences of Michael's idealism.

MICHAEL FARADAY, 1830
(painting by Pickersgill)

MICHAEL FARADAY, 1842
(painting by Phillips)

(*Courtesy of the Royal Institution*)

CHAPTER TEN

—And What Came of It

> Around the magnet Faraday
> Was sure that Volta's lightnings play:
>   But how to draw them from the wire?
> He took a lesson from the heart:
> 'Tis when we meet, 'tis when we part,
>   Breaks for the electric fire.
>
>   HERBERT MAYO

It is 23rd September 1831, and Faraday at the Royal Institution is writing to his friend Phillips. No doubt he is eager to convince him that the severance of their professional association does not affect their personal relations— the letter is mainly chit-chat—but he also wants him to be the very first to know that his decision already promises to be justified by results. He is cautious, however, in his report of progress: 'I am busy just now again on Electromagnetism, and think I have got hold of a good thing, but can't say; it may be a weed instead of a fish that after all my labour I may at last pull up.'

What he did pull up was not a weed; it was a whopper, the biggest catch of the century. The size of it can be fully appreciated only by reading the detailed report of the Institution of Electrical Engineers on the Centenary Celebrations held in London during the week including 23rd September 1931, when Michael's exploit was made the occasion of a second international congress in his honour. London was floodlighted throughout that week as never before; rightly so, for it was Michael who made floodlighting feasible. In this chapter only an outline of his memorable achievement can be presented, largely in his own words.

As far back as 1822, Michael had written in his notebook: 'Convert magnetism into electricity?' Yes, but how to do it? He made four trials between 1824 and 1828, all without result. Yet his intuition told him that success was possible, if only he could find the right method of experimenting, and Thompson relates how at this period he used to carry in his waistcoat pocket a small model of an electromagnetic circuit —a straight iron core about an inch long, surrounded by a few spiral turns of copper wire—which at spare moments he would take out and contemplate, using it thus objectively to concentrate his thoughts upon the problem to be solved. For meanwhile, during the years that the locust had eaten, others had shown that electricity could be converted into magnetism. First, in 1825, William Sturgeon, a Woolwich electrician, in early life a cobbler, and a gunner in the Royal Artillery for nearly twenty years, had coated an iron bar bent in the form of a horse-shoe with insulating varnish, wound it round with a long coil of bare copper wire (the turns of the coil not touching), passed an electric current through the wire, and found that the iron horse-shoe became an 'electromagnet' that would support the prodigious weight of nine pounds. Joseph Henry, a young teacher at Albany Academy, New York, improved on this by systematic winding with layer after layer of silk-covered copper wire, nine separate coils each sixty feet long with intervals between them along the horse-shoe. When all nine coils were joined up in parallel electric circuits, a lifting power of 650 pounds was obtained.

—And What Came of It

This was in 1830; now let us see what Michael did in 1831. His Diary, dated August 29, states:

'1. Expts. on the production of Electricity from Magnetism, etc., etc.

'2. Have had an iron ring made (soft iron), iron round and $\frac{7}{8}$ inches thick and ring 6 inches in external diameter. Wound many coils of copper wire round one half, the coils being separated by twine and calico—there were 3 lengths of wire each about 24 feet long and they could be connected as one length or used as separate lengths. By trial with a trough each was insulated from the other. Will call this side of the ring A. On the other side but separated by an interval was wound wire in two pieces together amounting to about 60 feet in length, the direction being as with the former coils; this side call B.

'3. Charged a battery of 10 pr. plates 4 inches square. Made the coil on B side one coil and connected its extremities by a copper wire passing to a distance and just over a magnetic needle (3 feet from iron ring). Then connected the ends of one of the pieces on A side with battery; immediately a sensible effect on needle. It oscillated and settled at last in original position. On *breaking* connection of A side with Battery again a disturbance of the needle.

'4. Made all the wires on A side one coil and sent current from battery through the whole. Effect on needle much stronger than before.'

A rough sketch of the ring used by Michael in these experiments—his old drawing-master Masquerier would not be very happy with it—is reproduced overleaf; the statue standing in the entrace hall of the Royal Institution (see the frontispiece to this volume) shows him holding that ring in his left hand.

—And What Came of It

Was he pleased or disappointed with these preliminary experiments? Probably the latter; he had hoped to obtain not a mere kick of the needle, but a permanent deflection indicating

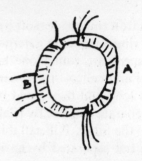

Faraday's Induction Ring
(Original sketch)

a continuous current passing through the B coil. The following day, modifying his set-up and observing stronger movements, still very short and sudden, at the moment of making and breaking the battery connection, he had an inspiration and wrote in his Diary:

'May not these transient effects be connected with causes of difference between power of metals in rest and in motion in Arago's expts.?'

What were 'Arago's expts.'? They had demonstrated, in 1824, a new phenomenon—called by its discoverer in Paris 'magnetism by rotation'—and it was this phenomenon that had induced Michael to make his previous fruitless trials. The initial stages of Arago's work may be omitted, it is the final result that is important here—that a flat disc of copper or, indeed, any conducting metal spinning directly below a suspended needle tends to drag the needle with it. As the rate of spin is increased, the needle is deflected more and more until finally it rotates with the disc. Conversely, other experimenters found that spinning a magnet under a pivoted metal disc made the disc revolve briskly. Nobody could explain it, but there it was.

Now Michael patiently rearranged his plans. First of all, he made his recording instruments more sensitive—any schoolboy of to-day would smile at his original apparatus—using a proper galvanometer (invented by Schweigger of Halle in 1820) to observe the induction of his electric currents. He stepped up the magnitude of these make-and-break currents until on October 1st they pulled the galvanometer needle right round: 'very powerful effect, but still it was only momentary.' The same day he was excited at seeing a spark pass between pencils of charcoal at the end of his inducing wires, 'very distinct though small, only at the moment of contact or disjunction'. More experiments followed, but his apparatus was even now too crude to show the results he expected to obtain, and ought to have obtained.

At long last, therefore, he decided to try what he could achieve with the help of a great compound steel magnet belonging to the Royal Society. All his experiments (Numbers 78–83 in his Diary) on October 27th had given negative results. Sliding plates, rotating wheels, nothing would work: 'Think it ought to do, yet got no effects.' He appended dejectedly: 'Prepared to go to Mr. Christie's to-morrow,' for this large magnet was at the moment on loan to his friend Mr. Christie at Woolwich.

To Woolwich therefore he travelled on October 28th. He performed many experiments, raising his score that day from 85 to 129. The great magnet responded beautifully; the old make-and-break contacts 'whirl the galvanometer needle round many times'. But it was when Michael topped his century mark, revolving a copper disc between the poles of the magnet, that the real climax arrived. 'The axis and edge of the disc were connected with a galvanometer. The needle moved as the disc turned. Effects were very distinct *and constant*.'

Thus, for the first time, a continuous electric current was 'produced from magnetism'. Supporters of the Arsenal Football Club will forgive me when I assert that this was the most important event in Woolwich history, for Michael had set in motion—and here, I hope, Moscow will also excuse me—the first dynamo.

And now he pressed forward in a frenzy never surpassed by Davy in his prime. On November 4th he was again at Mr. Christie's, testing all kinds of variations in his lay-out; some succeeded, some failed. Then he went into seclusion to prepare a connected account of his researches, presented before the Royal Society on November 24th. The contents of this epoch-making communication elicited the following comment from Professor W. Cramp when he delivered the Seventh Faraday Lecture of the Institution of Electrical Engineers in 1931:

'The paper contains far more than is noted in his diary, and shows what hard thinking he must have done during those three weeks. He sees clearly that there are two sets of phenomena. The first is that in which a varying current in one coil produces transient currents in a second coil. These he calls "*volta-electric induction*". They underlie every transformer (whether for power or for wireless), every coupled circuit, every induction coil that has since been made. The second set, in which the relative movement between a magnet and a coil or disc produces a current, he calls "*magneto-electric induction*", and these underlie every dynamo, alternator or motor since constructed. Thus then was born the industry of electrical engineering.'

After his day of exaltation at the Royal Society, Michael

let Sarah take him to Brighton for a brief holiday; he spent a part of it writing to Phillips on 'an extra large sheet of paper'. He started: 'News I have none, for I withdraw myself more and more from society, and all I have to say is about myself. I have been working and writing up a paper and that always knocks me up in health, but now I feel well again and will tell you what it is about.' Evidently Phillips had not attended the Royal Society meeting the previous week, but Michael was determined to bring him up-to-date, and did so, heedless of ink and paper. We need merely to note here Michael's particular pleasure that he had explained 'all Arago's phenomena, I believe, perfectly', and that he had got one up on the higher mathematicians: 'It is comfortable to me to find that experiment need not quail before mathematics, but is quite competent to rival it in discovery.'

Refreshed by Dr. Brighton, Michael plunged into the current again at the Royal Institution, and before the end of December he completed three new series of experiments. In the first, he dispensed with the man-made magnets previously used, and made 'that great magnet the earth' do the work instead. 'Tried Expts. on effect of terrestrial magnetism in evolving electricity,' he wrote in his Diary on December 14th, 'obtained beautiful results.' On Boxing Day he did away with the necessity for a moving conductor separate from the exciting magnet, he rotated a bar magnet itself about its axis, with wires attached to one end and to its centre, and a continuous electric current flowed through the galvanometer connected to the two wires. Finally (and again I quote from Professor Cramp), 'he simplified still further the "terrestrial dynamo" by reducing the coil to a single turn, thus inventing the "earth inductor" still to be seen at the Royal Institution. Industry, persistence and ingenuity could go no further than this last experiment of the year 1831. There is a fitting note of triumph in his final entry: "Experiments with a single wire. Beautiful." '

So ends his *Annus Mirabilis*. The results of the above experiments received the distinction of constituting the Bakerian Lecture of the Royal Society in January 1832, and Michael was to continue, and to expand, his researches on electricity for thirty more years, but it is obvious that this later work cannot be reported upon in such amplitude as has been accorded its initial stages. A sample was essential; one sample must suffice. In Chapter Thirteen the significance of his subsequent investigations will be summarized; we can relax until then and turn to more personal matters.

Michael had already notified Phillips in December 1831 that he was withdrawing himself more and more from society. As time went on, this process continued; his Journal includes an elaborate table of the things he gave up between 1834 and 1841. After 1834, for example, he declined 'all dining out or invitations', after 1838 he closed his doors three days in the week, 'saw no one'. This was absolutely necessary if he were to get ahead with his own work as he wished, for he was besieged by cranks of every kind and description. He himself noted plaintively: 'The number of suggestions, hints for discovery, and propositions of various kinds offered to me very freely, and with perfect goodwill and simplicity on the part of the proposers for my exclusive investigation and final honour, is remarkably great, and it is no less remarkable that but for one exception—that of Mr. Jenkin—they have all been worthless. The volunteers are serious embarrassments generally to the experienced philosopher.'

This one exception, Mr. Jenkin, merits a special paragraph. Tyndall tells us:

'On 29th January 1835, Faraday read before the Royal

—And What Came of It

Society a paper "On the influence by induction of an electric current upon itself". A shock and spark of a peculiar character had been observed by a young man named William Jenkin, who must have been a youth of some scientific promise, but who, as Faraday once informed me, was dissuaded by his own father from having anything to do with science. The investigation of the fact noticed by Mr. Jenkin led Faraday to the discovery of the *extra current*, or the current *induced in the primary wire itself* at the moments of making and breaking contact, the phenomena of which he described and illustrated in the beautiful and exhaustive paper referred to.'

It must not be imagined, however, that Michael developed into a modern Diogenes; he enjoyed company of his own choosing, particularly in his own family circle. Sarah's artist brother, George, says: 'All the years I was with Harding I dined at the Royal Institution. After dinner we nearly always had our games just like boys—sometimes at ball, or with horse chestnuts instead of marbles—Faraday appearing to enjoy them as much as I did, and generally excelling us all. Sometimes we rode around the theatre on a velocipede, which was then a new thing.' Regarding this velocipede, J. F. B. Firth informs us: 'It was probably a four-wheeled velocipede that Faraday was accustomed, some thirty years ago, to work his way up and down the steep roads near Hampstead and Highgate. This machine appears to have been of his own construction, and was worked by levers and a crank axle in the same manner as the rest of the four-wheeled class.'

His niece, Margaret Reid, who lived with Michael and Sarah at the Royal Institution for many years—the one regret of their marriage was that they had no children of their own—has recalled: 'Often of an evening they would go to the

—And What Came of It

Zoological Gardens and find interest in all the animals, especially the new arrivals, though he was always much diverted by the tricks of the monkeys. We have seen him laugh till the tears ran down his cheeks as he watched them. He never missed seeing the wonderful sights of the day—acrobats and tumblers, giants and dwarfs; even Punch and Judy was an unfailing source of delight, whether he looked at the performance or at the admiring gaping crowd.'

Although he relinquished service on the Council of the Royal Society, and later refused its presidency when it was offered him, he still maintained general scientific contacts. He frequently attended the meetings of the newly established British Association for the Advancement of Science; at its meeting at Oxford in 1832—when Keble, the Professor of Poetry, was very angry at the temper and tone of his colleagues, who had 'truckled sadly to the spirit of the times' in welcoming 'the hodge-podge of philosophers'—the honorary degree of D.C.L. was conferred upon him. Tyndall relates an 'exquisite morsel' from this meeting:

'Faraday was requested by some of the authorities to repeat the celebrated experiment of eliciting a spark from a magnet, employing for this purpose the large magnet in the Ashmolean Museum. To this he consented, and a large party assembled to witness the experiments, which, I need not say, were perfectly successful. Whilst he was repeating them a dignitary of the University entered the room and addressing himself to Professor Daniell, who was standing near Faraday, inquired what was going on. The Professor explained to him as popularly as possible this striking result of Faraday's great discovery. The Dean listened with attention and looked earnestly at the brilliant spark, but a moment after he assumed a serious countenance and shook his head: "I am sorry for it," said he, as he walked away; in the middle of the room he stopped for a moment and repeated, "I am sorry for it;" then walking towards the door, when the handle was in his hand he turned round and said, "*Indeed* I am sorry for it; it is putting new arms into the hands of the incendiary".'

One other occasion must be mentioned, the visit of Joseph Henry to Great Britain in 1837. Now Joseph Henry (page 114) was Michael's cleverest competitor, he actually duplicated Michael's fundamental discovery of electromagnetic induction early in 1832 before any account of that discovery had reached him. According to the Davy-Berzelius tradition, the two men should have been deadly enemies, but here is a reminiscence from Ames's *Memorials of Joseph Henry*:

'Henry loved to dwell on the hours that he and Bache had spent in Faraday's society. I shall never forget Henry's account of his visit to King's College, London, where Faraday, Wheatstone, Daniell, and he had met to try and evolve the electric spark from the thermopile. Each in turn attempted it and failed. Then came Henry's turn. He succeeded, calling in the aid of his discovery of the effect of a long inter-polar wire wrapped around a piece of soft iron. Faraday became as wild as a boy, and, jumping up, shouted: "Hurray for the Yankee experiment!" '

And if Michael could not foregather with his favourite confrères very frequently, he did at least write them letters. Never was there such a faithful correspondent; in 1836 he added to his already long list of pen-friends the name of Schönbein, professor of chemistry at Basle, the discoverer of ozone. Nearly ten years previously Schönbein, during a brief visit to London, had listened to one of Faraday's Friday Evening Lectures, but had been too shy to speak with him afterwards. Now he started to write to Michael on scientific topics, and their intimacy flourished until it became almost fraternal. The total of their interchanges, published after

—And What Came of It

their deaths, extends to about twice the length of the present book; it is indeed a delight to read, since it reveals the innermost thoughts and feelings of two eminent men.

But Michael's most cherished correspondents were still the De La Rives at Geneva. In 1835 he had the pleasure of meeting them once more, when Sarah accompanied him on a trip to Switzerland which his health demanded; did he recall his old vow (page 57) that he would never set foot out of England again? His letters to them are mainly 'philosophical', but every now and then human touches emerge. One communication to the elder De La Rive, dated 1845, concludes thus:

'Do you remember one hot day, I cannot tell how many years ago, when I was hot and thirsty in Geneva, and you took me to your house in town, and gave me a glass of water and raspberry vinegar? That glass of drink is refreshing to me still.

'Adieu, my dear friend. Remember me kindly to Madame De La Rive; and, if I am not too far wrong in the collection of thoughts and remembrance of past things, bring me to the mind of one or two young friends who showed me a doll's house once, and with whom I played on the green.'

Simple Mr. Faraday!

CHAPTER ELEVEN

A Pawn in Politics

I have rather, however, been desirous of discovering new facts and relations dependent on magneto-electric induction, than of exalting the force of those already obtained; being assured that the latter would find their full development hereafter.

MICHAEL FARADAY

I have sought no patent for inventions and solicited no remuneration for my labours, but have freely given their results to the world, expecting only in return to enjoy the consciousness of having added to the sum of human knowledge, and to receive the credit to which they may justly entitle me.

JOSEPH HENRY

These two quotations demonstrate how closely allied Faraday and Henry were in their worship of pure science and in their disregard of material reward. We may regret that they could not approximate more closely to the *golden medium* between theory and practice alluded to by Liebig on page 112; if they had, the development of electrical power production and utilization might have been advanced by fifty years. All the foundations for modern applications were available to any who cared to dig for them and to build upon them. May I give an example from my own experience? Forty years ago I was a young teacher at Columbia University in New York, and Michael Pupin—a Serbian peasant by birth, whose autobiography is told in *From Immigrant to Inventor*—was one of my very senior colleagues. Hearing that

A Pawn in Politics

I came from Scotland, Pupin related to me how he, as a student, once spent a holiday in the Isle of Arran, taking with him Faraday's *Collected Researches in Electricity*, bought as a bargain for three shillings at Cambridge. In spite of the competition of a Scots lassie, who interrupted Michael Pupin's reading of Michael Faraday by instruction in Highland reels, the result of that vacation was the invention of the loading coil used in reinforcing telephone circuits, the Pupin coil which first made long-distance telephony possible.

Very few inventors of Victorian times, however, did trouble to dig into Faraday's *Collected Researches*. It was not until 1868, the year after Michael's death, that a young man of twenty-one, Thomas Alva Edison, purchased a 'residue' set of Faraday's works in Boston and discovered that he had made his most profitable investment. He could understand Michael's simple, non-mathematical explanations; he could repeat Michael's clearly described experiments; he with his limited education regarded Michael as his master. Nobody, he remarked later, did anything in electricity at that period except telegraph operators and manufacturers of cheap apparatus for school science classes. How Edison changed all that is now familiar to everyone. Nevertheless, as J. S. Highfield said at the Centenary Celebrations in 1931: 'The time interval between Faraday's discoveries and the common use thereof was considerable, measured by the span of one man's life.' And Sir Josiah Stamp, speaking on *Electricity in Transport* at the same Celebrations, stated: 'Faraday's discoveries came at the beginning of the great steam era, and for 50 years there would have been no material difference in transport even if those discoveries had not been made. At a jubilee Faraday celebration, I doubt if an address could have been given on this subject.'

It would be unjust, however, to censure Michael in the

slightest degree for this delay. Made as he was, he could not act differently. As Tyndall remarks: 'Faraday was more than a philosopher; he was a prophet', and prophets rarely live to see their predictions fulfilled. The fault rested with the 'practical men' of the nineteenth century, not with Faraday.

Nineteenth-century prophets in London, nevertheless, were not fed by ravens; prophets' wives had to pay their own grocer's bills; and, by 1835, Michael's finances were in a deplorable condition. Since the silly fellow would do nothing for himself, his friends determined to do something for him. Headed by Sir James South—who only five years earlier had been protesting against the extravagant cost of the research on optical glass—they convinced Sir Robert Peel, then Prime Minister, that Michael was worthy of being granted a pension from the Civil List. 'I am sure', Peel said, 'no man living has a better claim to consideration from the State.' Before Peel could make the necessary recommendation, however, he was defeated in the House of Commons, and the opposite party came into power, led by Lord Melbourne. On April 20th, Sir James South first informed Michael how matters stood, and how he proposed now to present a petition to Melbourne. Michael thanked him for his goodwill but replied: 'I cannot accept a pension whilst I am able to work for my living. I think that Government is right in rewarding and sustaining science. I think that scientific men are not wrong in accepting pensions; but still I may not take a pay which is not for services performed.'

What could one do against such obstinacy? Sarah knew, she asked her father to use his persuasion, and after a heart-to-heart talk with Mr. Barnard (for whose judgment Michael always held the utmost respect) Michael modified his refusal. Still, much valuable time had been lost, and it was not until

A Pawn in Politics

October 26th that he was requested to wait upon Lord Melbourne at the Treasury. He was first interviewed by the Prime Minister's secretary, Thomas Young, to whom he detailed his religious scruples against receiving a pension, concluding with a homily on the immorality of savings banks, based no doubt on the text: 'Lay not up for yourselves treasures upon earth.' We can imagine the astonished Tom Young tapping his forehead significantly as he showed simple Michael into his Chief's private room, and whispering the nineteenth century equivalent of 'Nuts'!

At any rate Lord Melbourne, completely mistaking the nature of his visitor and prejudiced against him only because he was a protégé of Peel, entered into a diatribe on the whole principle of bestowing pensions upon literary and scientific persons, which he denounced brusquely as 'a piece of humbug'. The word humbug was prefixed by an adjective which Michael as a good Sandemanian could not write in his Journal, he merely noted that it was 'theological'. Solvers of crossword-puzzles, however, may appreciate the clue: 'mad dog—reversed'.

Now, as I have already remarked, Michael had an excitable and fiery temper; Tyndall tells us: 'Underneath his sweetness and gentleness was the heat of a volcano.' At Melbourne's words Vesuvius almost erupted, but Michael controlled himself, bowed, and immediately withdrew. That same evening he left this note, with his card, at Lord Melbourne's office:

'My Lord,

'The conversation with which your Lordship honoured me this afternoon, including, as it did, your Lordship's opinion of the general character of the pensions given of late to scientific persons, induces me respectfully to decline the favour which I believe your Lordship intends for me; for I feel that I could not, with satisfaction to myself, accept at your Lordship's hands that which, though it has the form of approbation, is of the character which your Lordship so pithily applied to it.'

From this point, the affair became a public political issue that almost overthrew the Melbourne Government. The events of October 26th are essentially accurate, since they are mostly extracted straight from Michael's Journal, but what ensues is open to the suspicion of party bias. *The Times* of November 28th printed almost a column under the head of 'Tory and Whig patronage to Science and Literature'. 'Lord Melbourne grossly insults the first chemist of his day', was its keynote. This outburst in *The Times* was based upon an article in *Fraser's Magazine*, which concludes the story thus:

'The dénouement was remarkable. Soon after these incidents, Lady Mary Fox chanced to visit Sir James South, on whose table she saw a small electrifying machine with a ticket on it indicating that "The machine . . . is the first of which Faraday ever came into possession." It stood when he was a youth in an optician's window in Fleet Street, and was offered for sale at the cost of 4s. 6d.; yet such was the low state of Faraday's finances that he could not purchase it. Many a day he came to the window to gaze, and went away again bitterly lamenting his own poverty, not because it subjected him to bodily inconvenience, but because it threatened to exclude him for ever from the path of science and usefulness, on which he longed to enter. At last he did succeed in purchasing it, and he now presented it to Sir James South. Lady Mary was greatly touched by this simple tale, she highly approved of the reply that Faraday had made to Lord Melbourne. The whole story was repeated to the King [William

IV], including an outline of Faraday's early struggles with poverty, and the Monarch was so affected by the narrative that he shed tears; "that man deserves all the pension that Peel promised," said the King, "and he shall have it too." So Lord Melbourne is informed that, whatever his Lordship's feelings might be, those of William the Fourth are the feelings of a gentleman. And Faraday is, after all, to accept the pension— not as a gift from the Whig Cabinet, but directly from the King.'

Of course the press on the other side counter-attacked. *The Courier* of December 7th carried an editorial commenting upon the 'imaginary conversation' published in *The Times* and saying: 'The person most insulted and most injured by it is Mr. Faraday, who will be suspected by the whole kingdom, unless he contradict it in his own name, of having authorised the publication and supplied the scanty proportion of truth which was woven into the web of fiction.' The next day a letter from Michael appeared in *The Times*, stating: 'I beg leave thus publicly to state that neither directly nor indirectly did I communicate to the editor of *Fraser's Magazine* the information on which that article was founded, or further, either directly or indirectly, any information to or for any publication whatsoever.'

All this fuss was really quite unnecessary, for meanwhile the matter had been amicably settled. Bence Jones informs us: 'An excellent lady, who was a friend both to Faraday and the Minister, tried to arrange matters between them; but she found Faraday very difficult to move from the position he had assumed. After many fruitless efforts, she at length begged of him to state what he would require of Lord Melbourne to induce him to change his mind. He replied, 'I should require from his Lordship what I have no right or reason to expect that he would grant—a written apology for the words he permitted himself to use to me.' Melbourne, however, did write to Michael on November 24th expressing deep concern at the consequences of his 'blunt and inconsiderate manner', and the hope that he would now 'have the satisfaction of receiving your consent to my advising His Majesty to grant you a pension'. Michael immediately replied: 'My Lord, your Lordship's letter, which I have just had the honour to receive, has occasioned me both pain and pleasure—pain, because I should have been the cause of your Lordship's writing such an one, and pleasure, because it assures me that I am not unworthy of your Lordship's regard. I hesitate not to say I shall receive your Lordship's offer both with pleasure and with pride.' A pension of £300 a year was officially announced on December 24th, and Sarah at least enjoyed a 'Merry Christmas'.

Michael himself was still touchy about the whole business; he hated publicity and when, in 1837, he received a note from the Chancellor of the Exchequer stating that it would be his 'duty in the early part of the present session to move for a committee to inquire how far the existing pensions ought to be continued, having due regard to the just claims of the parties and to economy in the public expenditure' he answered, 'If the grant do not retain the same feeling and character as that which Lord Melbourne attached to it, I should, though with all respect to the Government, certainly have no wish for its continuance.' He was *not* amused by a second article that appeared in *Fraser's Magazine* in February 1836, which showed a picture of him on the lecture platform: 'Here you have him in his glory—not that his position was *inglorious* when he stood before Melbourne, then decorated with a blue velvet travelling cap, and lounging with one leg over the chair of Canning!—and distinctly gave that illustrious despiser of "humbug" to understand that he had mistaken his lad. No! but here you have him as he first flashed upon the intelligence of mankind the condensation of the gases, or the identity of the five electricities.' After a breezy résumé of Michael's career and the jocular suggestion that Far-a-day must be near-a-knight, the article continued: 'The future Baronet is a very good little fellow playing a fair fork over a leg of mutton, and devoid of any reluctance to partake an old friend's third bottle. We know of few things more agreeable than a cigar and a bowl of punch (which he mixes admirably) in the society of the unpretending ex-bookbinder.'

All this, of course, is pure journalese. Far-a-day was ne'er-a-knight, every offer in that direction was firmly declined, he remarked to Tyndall once: 'Tyndall, I must remain plain Michael Faraday to the last.' He was, it is true, 'a good little fellow'—like Davy, he was below middle height—but phrenologists will be interested to know that his head was so long from front to back that he usually had to bespeak his hats. As to his being a 'three-bottle man', well, I ask you! and with regard to cigars, we have his niece's direct testimony: 'the smell of tobacco was disagreeable to him.' No, Michael was not a typical Tory of that period; he was above all politics.

And he got even with the Government on his pension after all. In a letter to the First Lord of the Admiralty, Lord Auckland, he stated in 1847: 'I have given up, for the last ten years or more, all professional occupation, and voluntarily resigned a large income that I might pursue my own objects of research. But in doing this I have always, as a good subject, held myself ready to assist the Government if still in my power—*not for pay*, for, except in one instance (and then only for the sake of the person joined with me), I refused to take it. I have had the honour and pleasure of applications, and that very recently from the Admiralty, the Ordnance, the Home

A Pawn in Politics

Office, the Woods and Forests, and other departments, all of which I have replied to, and will reply to as long as strength is left me.' His nominal salary of £200 a year as scientific adviser to the Admiralty he never drew. One thing he would *not* do was to act as expert witness in court. After an occasion when, the scientific evidence from the two sides having been very discordant, the judge remarked: 'Science has not shone this day,' Michael steadfastly refused all work of this character. Nobody was going to have the opportunity to insult *him* twice!

Among the multitude of public services he rendered—services that repaid his pension sevenfold—one is of especial interest. In 1844, he was asked to investigate, in conjunction with Sir Charles Lyell, the famous geologist, a terrible pit accident that had occurred at Haswell Colliery, near Durham. The inquest disclosed that there had been reprehensible carelessness in the mine; one witness stated: 'Men can light a pipe by a Davy lamp. Smoking is strictly forbidden, but men will smoke sometimes; it is a very great evil.' Sir Charles Lyell, furthermore, recounts the following incident:

'We spent eight hours, not without danger, in exploring the galleries where the chief loss of life had been incurred. Among other questions, Faraday asked in what way they measured the rate at which the current of air flowed in the mine. An inspector took a small pinch of gunpowder out of a box, as he might have taken a pinch of snuff, and allowed it to fall gradually through the flame of a candle which he held in the other hand. His companion, with a watch, marked the time the smoke took going a certain distance. Faraday admitted that this plan was sufficiently accurate for their purpose; but, observing the somewhat careless manner in which they handled their powder, he asked where they kept it. They said they kept it in a bag, the neck of which was tied up tight.

"But where," said he, "do you keep the bag?" "You are sitting on it," was the reply.'

This mission, incidentally, was the single mission for which Michael, as mentioned in his letter to Lord Auckland, accepted pay. Typically enough, he did not accept it for his own use, however, as Lyell relates: 'Hearing that a subscription had been opened for the widows and orphans of the men who had perished by the explosion, I found, on inquiry, that Faraday had already contributed largely. On speaking to him on the subject, he apologised for having done so without mentioning it to me, saying that he did not wish me to feel myself called upon to subscribe because he had done so.'

In 1836 he did take on one additional permanent appointment, that of scientific adviser to the Trinity House, the body in official charge of English lighthouses. For this responsibility he received what the Deputy-Master regarded as the totally inadequate sum of £200 a year, but as Michael himself said in his letter of acceptance: 'I can at any moment convert my time into money, but I do not require more of the latter than is sufficient for necessary purposes. The sum, therefore, of £200 is quite enough in itself, but not if it is to be the indicator of the character of the appointment; but I think you do not view it so, and that you and I understand each other in that respect.' And Bence Jones tells us: 'For thirty years nearly he held this post. What he did may be seen in the portfolios, full of manuscripts, which Mrs. Faraday has given to the Trinity House, in which, by the marvellous order and method of his notes and indices, each particle of his work can be found and consulted immediately.'

Looking back, we can have no doubt that this was a wise move. Michael's considered opinion in 1860 may be quoted: 'There is no part in my life which gives me more delight than my connection with the Trinity House. The occupation of nations joined together to guide the mariner over the sea, to all a point of great interest, is infinitely more so to those who are concerned in the operations which they carry into effect; and it certainly has astonished me, since I have been connected with the Trinity House, to see how beautifully and how wonderfully shines forth among nations at large the desire to do good.'

His frequent visits to lighthouses all round the English coast afforded him much-needed relaxation at intervals of overwork, and the value of the advice that he gave on all varieties of problems—notably lighthouse ventilation (see page 104) and the application of electric lighting to lighthouses —cannot be overestimated. Sarah's mind could now be at rest; that wolf had been driven from her door again.

CHAPTER TWELVE

The Long, Long Trail. I

The electro-magnet was excited and rendered neutral; but not the slightest effect on the polarized or unpolarized ray [from lines in various flame spectra] was observed.

Faraday's Diary (12th March 1862)

That is the final sentence in Michael's manuscript record of his experimental researches in magnetism and electricity, written more than thirty years after he penned the first paragraph on 29th August 1831. How many separate experiments did he make in the interval? One cannot state the exact total—since he included some on chemical subjects on the one hand, while he stopped numbering the entries in his old age on the other hand—but the last consecutive figure is 16,041.

I have already promised (page 120) not to describe his later researches, monumental though they are, in minute detail. This chapter will be devoted to a general discussion of his manifold activities, in Chapter Thirteen some of the more significant topics will receive specific mention.

First of all, it is important to appreciate Michael's particular advantages and disadvantages in his super-Marathon pursuit of the Spirit of Truth. His greatest asset, perhaps, was his power of anticipation. This anticipation was partly intuitive—years before the law of the conservation of energy, for example, had been established, Michael *knew* that it ought to be possible, given the proper apparatus, to demonstrate the conversion of any one kind of energy into any other. All the varieties of electricity—frictional, galvanic, voltaic, magnetic and thermal—must be fundamentally identical; all forces—electrical, magnetic, optical, thermal, chemical, mechanical, even gravitational—must exercise mutual effects upon each other. This was the primary article of his scientific faith, and this led him to his most magnificent discoveries. Kohlrausch said of him: 'Er riecht die Wahrheit' (He smells the truth).

But his anticipation was also, to the highest degree, due to his peculiar capacity for considering all possibilities in advance. His brain went always well ahead of his hands in experimental work, and yet he was ever watchful for something unexpected, seldom failing to fathom its significance. Tyndall remarks in this connection: 'Faraday has been called a purely inductive philosopher. A great deal of nonsense is, I fear, uttered about induction and deduction. Some profess to befriend the one, some the other, while the real vocation of an investigator like Faraday consists in the incessant marriage of both.'

Other factors that favoured Michael were methodicalness and bulldog pertinacity. The chaos that reigned in Davy's laboratory was replaced by apple-pie order from the moment Michael entered it. And he never would confess himself beaten; however often a crucial experiment might fail, back he would come to it, attacking at a new angle. A year, five years, ten years might elapse, still he would go on trying. Gladstone tells us: 'His tenacity of purpose showed itself equally in little and in great things. Arranging some apparatus one day with a philosophical instrument maker, he let fall on the floor a small piece of glass: he made several ineffectual attempts to pick it up. "Never mind," said his companion, "it is not worth the trouble." "Well, but, Murray, I don't like to be beaten by something that I have once tried to do." '

Now let us turn our attention to Michael's handicaps. One was certainly his lack of a formal education, especially in mathematics. He was ignorant of all but the merest elements of arithmetic, but when Clerk Maxwell, the greatest British mathematical physicist of the century, made an exhaustive theoretical examination of *Faraday's Lines of Force* in 1855, he found not the slightest flaw in any of the conclusions Michael drew from his experimental results. And Helmholtz, the greatest European mathematical physicist of the century, remarked in his Faraday Lecture in 1881 : 'It is in the highest degree astonishing to see what a large number of general theorems, the methodical deduction of which requires the highest powers of mathematical analysis, he found by a kind of intuition, with the security of instinct, without the help of a single mathematical formula.' Michael himself gloried in beating the mathematicians at their own game (see page 119), and used to boast that only once in his whole life had he performed a mathematical operation—when he turned the handle of Babbage's calculating machine. Yet he must frequently have spent hours hammering out problems that even mediocre mathematicians could have solved in a flash, and he occasionally butted his head against a brick wall when better knowledge would have warned him that he was attempting the impossible. It is noteworthy that he once made the naïve suggestion to Clerk Maxwell that mathematicians should publish their results in duplicate, the second copy translating their 'hieroglyphics' into common language for the convenience of experimental workers.

A second drag upon his progress was the poverty of the Royal Institution, which often forced him to work with apparatus quite inadequate for his needs. Nevertheless, he was not averse to going elsewhere, as to Mr. Christie's, to employ more powerful instruments when in dire extremity, and he was unsurpassed in his ability to secure exact and unequivocal results with the crudest equipment. Again, it must be emphasized that much time, and many disappointments, would have been saved him if more money had been at his disposal for precise experimentation. 'Penny-wise, pound-foolish' was British policy with respect to pure science in that material age. Michael's very last experiment, you will note, was a failure, but in 1897 the effect he was looking for was discovered by Zeeman.

Other much more significant relationships for which Michael searched many years in vain waited even longer for experimental confirmation. One example is sufficiently important to warrant a short digression. Nothing that Michael ever did excited more scepticism than his persistent efforts to establish a direct connection between gravitational and other forces. Patient investigations in his laboratory at the Royal Institution, in the Clock Tower of the Houses of Parliament and in the old shot-tower still standing near the south end of Waterloo Bridge in the grounds of the Festival of Britain, invariably ended in results that were completely negative and evoked in certain quarters expressions of open derision. Yet Michael never lost heart; an entry in his Diary dated 25th August 1849 indicates how clearly he appreciated the cardinal significance of his conviction that some link *must* exist:

'I have been arranging certain experiments in reference to the notion that gravity itself may be practically and directly related by experiment to the other powers of matter and this morning proceeded to make them. It was almost with a feeling of awe that I went to work—for if the hope should prove well founded how great and mighty and sublime in its hitherto unchangeable character is the force I am trying to deal with, and how large may be the new domain of knowledge that may be opened up to the mind of man.'

Another note appended to his preliminary plan of campaign reads: 'All this is a dream. Still examine it by a few experiments. Nothing is too wonderful to be true, if it be consistent with the laws of nature, and in such things as these, experiment is the best test of such consistency.' The experiments that he actually performed were far from few, and ten years later he returned to the attack with the remark: 'Must not be deterred by the old experiments.' But as Sir William Bragg, then himself Director of the Royal Institution, stated in 1931 at the Centenary Celebrations of the Institution of Electrical Engineers: 'Of course he failed in this attempt; the links for which he sought were far beyond his powers of discovery, limited as they were by the apparatus and the knowledge of his time. In principle he was perfectly right, and the words that he used are now applicable to those strange connections between gravity and light which are involved in the theory of relativity.' For when Einstein's calculations based on this theory, that a ray of light from a distant star passing near the rim of the sun on its journey to the earth ought to be deflected through a small angle by the sun's gravitational field, were tested at a number of observatories during the lar eclipses of 1919 and 1922 and found to be quantitatively correct, Michael's dream was recognized as a reality after all.

Did Michael ever suspect that it might be necessary to work on a cosmic scale, rather than within the limit of 165 feet afforded him by his shot-tower, to demonstrate this reality? It almost appears so, for a further entry in his Diary on 25th August 1849 runs: 'If there should be any truth in these vague expectations of the relation of Gravitating force, then it seems hardly possible but that there must be some extraordinary results to come out in relation to celestial mechanics—as between the earth and the moon, or the Sun and the planets, or in the great space between all gravitating bodies. Then indeed, Milton's expression of the Sun's magnetic ray would have a real meaning in addition to its poetical one.' Michael, it may be noted, was well-read not only in Milton, but in all the great English poets, though he did not share Davy's facility in writing original verse.

His association with Davy was both helpful and detrimental to him. Helpful, inasmuch as he inherited Humphry's experimental wizardry; detrimental, inasmuch as he modelled himself too closely on Humphry as a scientist (his criticism at the head of Chapter Six refers solely to Humphry's personal frailties) and carried his fidelity to excess. Here is an instance of Michael's imitative idolatry. In his very first letter to Abbott in 1812 he describes a repetition of one of Humphry's experiments thus:

'I, Sir, I my own self, cut out seven discs of the size of half-pennies each! I, Sir, covered them with seven halfpence, and I interposed between, seven, or rather six, pieces of paper soaked in a solution of muriate of soda!!! But laugh no longer, dear A.; rather wonder at the effects this trivial power produced. It was sufficient to produce the decomposition of sulphate of magnesia—an effect which extremely surprised me.' And his Diary of 26th September 1833 records the passage of a current through fused magnesium chloride: 'At negative pole, magnesium burnt, flying off in globules burning brilliantly. VERY GOOD EXPT.' Almost an exact replica, it will be noted, of Humphry's CAPITAL EXPT. with potassium (page 98). But Humphry's dogmas had the authority of Holy Writ to Michael even after Humphry's death; could he not recognize that nobody changed his opinions more quickly than Humphry living?

The most conspicuous example of Michael's fanaticism is his attitude towards Dalton and the atomic theory. He regarded Dalton as a 'much over-rated man', and his chemical publications, like Davy's, do not include one chemical formula. He did not even modify his opinion of Dalton as Davy did in 1826 when, as President of the Royal Society conferring on Dalton its first Royal Medal, he called him 'the highest and immortal ornament of this Society'. Humphry's views evidently, after the break in 1824, became suspect; but everything Humphry said before then was sacred. What a disadvantage this was to Michael in his chemical investigations will be demonstrated later (pages 150–1).

Michael's biggest liability of all, unfortunately, was his health. In 1841 he suffered the first of a series of nervous breakdowns—he had had several warnings long before 1841 —and for four years his experimental researches on electricity practically ceased. Sarah and her brother George accompanied him on a long holiday to Switzerland. His Journal of the trip is just as voluminous and as fascinating as that of his Grand Tour of Europe in 1813–15, but I must restrict myself here to an extract from a letter which Sarah wrote to Magrath: 'He certainly enjoys the country exceedingly, and though at first he lamented our absence from home and friends very much, he seems now to be reconciled to it as a means of improving his general health. His strength is, however, very good; he thinks nothing of walking thirty miles in a day (and very rough walking it is, you know), and one day he walked forty-five, which I protested against his doing again, though he was very little the worse for it. But the grand thing is rest and relaxation of mind, which he is really taking.'

The Long, Long Trail. I

Bence Jones states, 'His only illness was overwork, and his only remedy was rest,' and other biographers generally concur. I venture to disagree; an eminent university physician advised me once that in his long experience he had treated hundreds of cases of nervous breakdown, and he was convinced that the real cause was overwork in only five instances among students, and in no instance among the faculty. The primary factor, almost invariably, was worry, frequently dating back to many years previously.

Now a remarkable parallelism between Isaac Newton and Faraday may be noted. Both had natural genius of the same prophetic and simple type, both worked extremely hard, both were easily annoyed, both suffered from severe nervous breakdowns at the age of fifty, both recovered (Faraday more fully than Newton) to be honoured as still the most brilliant intellects of their respective eras, though shorn of some of their former splendour, for another generation.

Newton's contemporaries might ascribe his breakdown to overwork, but it is now understood that the main reason was prolonged worry. As Lord Keynes said at the Newton Tercentenary Celebrations, there was 'a dreadful secret which Newton was at desperate pains to conceal all his life', namely the fact that he, a Fellow of Trinity, was at heart an Arian and did not believe in the Trinity. How this inconsistency gnawed upon his conscience is evident from the masses of religious pamphlets that he wrote, hidden for centuries in the 'Portsmouth Box'. In the case of Faraday, his Sandemanian principles as we shall see in Chapter Fifteen—occasioned him no qualms; it was his 'god on earth', Humphry Davy, who tortured him. What mental agonies Michael must have undergone during his disagreements with Humphry! He must have felt like the Israelites when their Jehovah struck them down with plague and pestilence. The preliminary symptoms of his later trouble, 'loss of memory' and 'dizziness in the head', are mentioned again and again in his correspondence of those and subsequent years.

It would be wrong, however, for us to take Michael's own statements and those of his sympathetic intimates regarding his mental deterioration in middle life too literally. His research achievements and lecturing activities between 1842 and 1862 show beyond all shadow of doubt that he remained, despite his affliction, supreme among the scientists of that period. His declension was merely relative, he still stood head and shoulders above all others.

We may safely assume that the canny Town Councillors of Edinburgh, when they invited him to accept the chair of chemistry at their University in 1844, were satisfied in advance that he was competent to discharge all the duties of that office. A first-hand description of Faraday's proficiency in the eighteen-forties, provided by an eminent Irish scientist, Robert Mallet, deserves quotation in full:

'I was never in London without paying him a visit, and on one of those times I ventured to ask him (if not too much engaged) to let me see where he and Davy worked together. With the most simple graciousness he brought me through the whole of the Royal Institution, Albemarle Street. Brande's furnaces, Davy's battery, the place in the laboratory where he told me he had first observed the liquefaction of chlorine, are all vividly before me—but nothing so clear or vivid as our conversation over a specimen of green (crown) glass, partially devitrified in floating opaque white spheres of radiating crystals: he touched luminously on the obscure relation of the vitreous and crystalloid states, and on the probable nature of the nuclei of the white spheres. My next visit to Faraday that I recollect was not long after my paper "On the Dynamics of Earthquakes" had appeared in the Transactions of the Royal Irish Academy [1848]. He almost at once referred to it in terms of praise that seemed to me so far beyond my due, that even now I recall the very humble way I felt, as the thought of Faraday's own transcendent merits rushed across my mind. I ventured to ask him, had the paper engaged his attention sufficiently that I might ask him—did he consider my explanation of the before supposed *vorticose* shock sufficient? To my amazement he at once recited *nearly word for word* the paragraph in which I took some pains to put my views into a demonstrative shape, and ended with, "It is as plain and certain as a proposition of Euclid!" And yet the subject was one pretty wide away from his own subjects of study.'

Not much evidence of mental deficiency there! Another Irish-born scientist, no less a person than Lord Kelvin, carries our diagnosis into the next decade:

'For many years after 1850 my chief attraction for making a journey from Glasgow to London was always a visit to the Royal Institution to see Faraday—at home in the midst of his work. Bright, lively, kind, he showed me what he was doing. He spoke to me of it, and he encouraged me to go on with any work I could take up, either in connection with electricity or any of the other interesting and important things in physical science in which he was working and making discoveries. His encouragement to me was most valuable. I treasure it now, and I can look back upon it as an inspiring influence throughout my life. Faraday had the gift of inspiration.'

Is there any significance in Michael's readiness to receive Hibernian visitors in his laboratory, from which distinguished men of other nationalities (see page 153) were liable to be rigorously excluded?

The Long, Long Trail. I

Perhaps the greatest proof of Michael's abiding genius is the feeling of frustration he induced in those who followed him. Tyndall may first be cited in the following condensed extract:

'I have worked long myself at magne-crystallic action, amid all the light of Faraday's researches. His papers were objects of daily and nightly study with me eighteen or nineteen years ago; but even now, though their perusal is but the last of a series of repetitions, they astonish me. Every circumstance connected with the subject; every shade of deportment; every variation in the energy of the action; almost every application which could possibly be made of magnetism to bring out in detail the character of this new force, is minutely described. The field is swept clean, and hardly anything experimental is left for the gleaner.'

Similarly, Clerk Maxwell wrote:

'After nearly half a century of labour, we may say that, though the practical applications of Faraday's discovery have increased and are increasing in number and value every year, no exception to the statement of these laws as given by Faraday has been discovered, no new law has been added to them, and Faraday's original statement remains to this day the only one which asserts no more than can be verified by experiment, and the only one by which the theory of the phenomena can be expressed in a manner which is exactly and numerically accurate, and at the same time, within the range of elementary methods of exposition.'

Finally, Lord Kelvin remarked in 1896:

'One word characterises the most strenuous of the efforts for the advancement of science that I have made perseveringly during fifty-five years; that word is Failure. I know no more of electric and magnetic force, or of the relation between ether, electricity and ponderable matter, or of chemical affinity, than I knew and tried to teach to my students of natural philosophy fifty years ago.'

This despondency and this self-depreciation, of course, were overdone and overdrawn; all three of the men quoted above had originated most important advances; not even a Faraday can anticipate the march of scientific progress completely or indefinitely. The pessimistic belief prevalent among physicists towards the close of the nineteenth century that no major discoveries remained to be made has since been shattered by the most spectacular series of developments that any single science has ever witnessed, ranging from Röntgen-rays and radioactivity to radar, atomic fission and atomic fusion. Yet even in 1931 Einstein could say: 'I believe that future generations have yet as much to learn as has been learnt in the past from Faraday's conception of the electro-magnetic field.'

CHAPTER THIRTEEN

The Long, Long Trail. II

The principal result of Faraday's labours is our ability to use electricity. Prometheus, they say, brought fire to the service of mankind: electricity we owe to Faraday.

SIR WILLIAM BRAGG

It is indeed a difficult task to condense thirty years of experimental work by Michael Faraday into one chapter of reasonable length. If I were to mention all the topics that he investigated, the list would be about as comprehensive as a telephone directory and probably not any more interesting, since it would be impracticable to append any discussion. If I were to concentrate upon a single topic, as in Chapter Ten, the picture presented would be quite inadequate and misleading. I have therefore decided to adopt a middle course, selecting a limited number of the most significant projects and attempting to indicate, albeit briefly, Michael's method of attack and the main conclusions reached in each case.

Faraday's *Experimental Researches in Electricity and Magnetism* alone extend into twenty-nine series, occupying three large volumes, so that very rigorous thinning-out is obviously essential. And here let me make a confession: I have been influenced in my embarrassment of riches by the fact that in these days of specialization no one person is competent to cover Faraday's wide field. Perhaps the policy that I have pursued—not to try to describe to the lay reader any-

The Long, Long Trail. II

thing I cannot clearly comprehend myself—may prove to be prudent after all. I am not, primarily, a physicist, and although most of this chapter is severely and unavoidably physical the reader will, I trust, appreciate my relief when Michael reverts—as he does at intervals—to some simpler problem connected with his first love, chemistry. These relaxations of his later years would have established the reputation of any lesser man, and are eminently worthy of fleeting attention.

Michael's first major feat, after completing his work on the conversion of magnetism into electricity in 1831, was to demonstrate the identity of the five electricities (p. 137). Early workers—Galvani, Volta and even Davy—had drawn vain distinctions between electricity derived from different sources, and Michael did not want any doubt to arise as to the nature of the electric current that he had obtained from magnets by induction. He began by showing that an electrical discharge from a friction machine could deflect a galvanometer and could bring about chemical decompositions, just as voltaic electricity and his own magneto-electricity could do. Continuing his experiments, he drew up in tabular form a list of the effects that each 'different' electricity could be made to produce, and arrived in 1833 at the conclusion: 'Electricity, whatever may be its source, is identical in its nature.'

The next step was to try to establish quantitative relationships and this led him to an intensive study of the electrochemistry of solutions. Those who chatter glibly now about electrical units—amps, volts, ohms, watts, etc., all named after the great pioneers—will find it difficult to realize what a mess the subject was in at that time. The distinction between intensity and quantity was only just dawning; there were no recognized units. Faraday helped to clear up that mess; much of present-day terminology was actually invented by him, taking guidance from his classical friend Whewell. The two poles of an electric battery he called *electrodes* (the doors through which the current passes); the positive pole he called the *anode* (this way up!), the negative the *cathode* (this way down!). The conducting liquid between the poles he called an *electrolyte*; the passage of a current through this liquid, decomposing it, he called *electrolysis*. The products of decomposition proceeding to the anode he called *anions*; those going to the cathode he called *cations*. When he wanted to refer to both together, he called them *ions* (Greek, travellers).

To keep my promise of not going into details, I must omit all the intervening steps in Michael's electrochemical researches—the first quantitative work ever done in that field, for which purpose he devised the first coulometer—and jump immediately to the grand finale, still known as *Faraday's Law*. This states that equal quantities of electricity discharge equivalent quantities of the ions at the two electrodes, whatever those ions may be. By equivalent quantities Michael simply means the combining weights of the positive and negative radicals of the electrolyte, as determined by chemical analysis. When those weights are expressed in grammes, the quantity of electricity required is that known to-day as a *faraday*. (This must not be confused with another electrical unit, the *farad*, which is a unit of capacity; Michael's work on specific inductive capacity is too technical for description here.)

If only Michael had not regarded the atomic theory as an 'arbitrary conception', if only he had not fettered himself to the Wollaston-Davy limit of 'equivalents', what further advances he might have made! He does, it is true, in considering the theoretical implications of his law, condescend to say: 'If we adopt the atomic theory or phraseology, then the atoms of bodies which are equivalents to each other in their ordinary chemical action, have equal quantities of electricity naturally associated with them.' But he follows this up at once with: 'I must confess I am jealous of the term *atom*; for though it is very easy to talk of atoms, it is very difficult to form a clear idea of their nature.' His detraction of Dalton's ideas was all that prevented him from leaping far into the future, for here (says Thompson) we find the modern doctrine of *electrons*, or unitary atomic charges, clearly formulated in 1834!

On his return from his enforced holiday in Switzerland in 1841 Michael was still unfit to resume serious research work, although he managed to lecture frequently at the Royal Institution and to perform his duties for the Trinity House. In 1843, he diverted himself by harking back to an old field— the condensation of gases. By expert manipulation at high pressures and low temperatures, he effected the liquefaction, and even the solidification, of many new gases, and anticipated the results of later workers on 'critical constants' by predicting that in those cases where he still failed—such as hydrogen, oxygen and nitrogen—'no compression, without the conjoint application of a degree of cold below that we have as yet obtained, can be expected to take from them their gaseous state.'

That is all I can say regarding Faraday's work on gases,[1] but it is proper to add that his prophecy was fulfilled when a subsequent professor of chemistry at the Royal Institution, Sir James Dewar, the inventor of the thermos flask, brought even such a refractory gas as hydrogen to heel.

For many years before his nervous breakdown, Michael

[1] A complete account of both his earlier and later work constitutes Reprint Number 12 of the Alembic Club, *The Liquefaction of Gases*, obtainable from E. & S. Livingstone, Teviot Place, Edinburgh.

had been working and speculating on the effect of electricity on rays of light. There *must* be, he argued, correlation between electrical and optical energy; he tried to find it five times, and failed. His first attempt was on 10th September 1822. On 30th August 1845, he set out on his sixth attempt, sending polarized light—light in which the wave-vibrations are confined to one plane by passage through a Nicol prism[1]—through liquids undergoing electrolysis. Again failure, so he sent his polarized ray through a great variety of substances under strong electrostatic tension. Still failure, although the effect he sought for was discovered with more 'sensible' apparatus by Kerr thirty-two years later. Now he substituted magnetic for electrical forces, passing polarized light through transparent bodies placed between the poles of an electromagnet. All sorts of materials were examined rigorously without the slightest success. Then, on September 13th, he remembered his 'heavy glass', on the manufacture of which he had wasted four precious years of his youth. He tried it *and it worked*; the plane of the polarized ray was twisted by the magnetic field! His Diary for that lucky thirteenth concludes with Experiment 7,536 and the remark: 'Have got enough for to-day.' On September 18th he borrowed the Woolwich magnet and obtained a much stronger rotation of the ray; Experiment 7,610 records his delight: 'An excellent day's work.'

His triumph was reported to the Royal Society at its meeting on November 6th, but on November 4th Michael had already made a new discovery! Characteristically, he informed De La Rive of this before it was published; in the early part of a very long letter he tells his 'dear friend': 'Of late I have

[1] The principle of this is fully described in my book *Great Discoveries by Young Chemists* (Thomas Nelson and Sons, 1953). Space does not permit its repetition here.

FARADAY AND HIS BAR OF HEAVY GLASS
(*Courtesy of the Royal Institution*)

shut myself up in my laboratory and wrought, to the exclusion of everything else. I heard afterwards that even your brother had called on one of these days and been excluded. I am still so involved in discovery that I hardly have time for my meals.' Then he goes on to describe his latest achievement: 'If a cubical or rounded piece of my glass be suspended by a fine thread six or eight feet long, and allowed to hang very near a strong magneto-electric pole (not as yet made active), then on rendering the pole magnetic the glass will be repelled, and continue repelled until the magnetism ceases. This effect or power I have worked out through a great number of its forms and strange consequences. It is curious that amongst the metals are found bodies possessing this property in as high a degree as perhaps any other substance. In fact, I do not know at present whether heavy glass, or bismuth, or phosphorus is the most striking in this respect.'

Michael's memoir on 'The Magnetic Condition of All Matter' was communicated to the Royal Society on December 18th; *all* substances are either *diamagnetic*, repelled by a strong magnetic field, or *magnetic* (later he used the term *paramagnetic*), attracted by a strong magnetic field. He enumerated a long list, and concludes: 'It is curious to see such a list as this of bodies presenting on a sudden this remarkable property, and it is strange to find a piece of wood, or beef, or apple, obedient to or repelled by a magnet. If a man could be suspended with sufficient delicacy after the manner of Dufay, and placed in the magnetic field, he would point equatorially, for all the substances of which he is formed, including the blood, possess this property.'

I must move forward more rapidly, however, or I may be suspended not equatorially, but cervically. I shall merely mention a most important paper that Michael contributed to the *Philosophical Magazine* in May 1846, entitled 'Thoughts on Ray-vibrations'; it is one of the few speculative articles he ever published and it was totally ignored by his contemporaries. Tyndall dismisses it as 'one of the most singular speculations that ever emanated from a scientific man', Bence Jones follows his example, Gladstone does not even refer to it, but Thompson could assert in 1901: 'In this avowedly speculative paper Faraday touched the highest point in his scientific writings, and threw out, though in a tentative and fragmentary way, brilliant hints of that which his imagination had perceived, as in a vision—the doctrine now known as the electromagnetic theory of light.'

Now, in 1954, we can find in Faraday's suggestion that the ultimate particles of matter are not the discrete, immutable specks of Dalton, but centres of force stretching out into infinite space—a conception that renders, as he states, the nineteenth-century ether superfluous—an almost miraculous prognostication of modern opinions.

From 1847 to 1850, Michael was engaged on a long series of investigations on the magnetism of flame and of gases in general. Here I am forced to confine my comments to the consequences of the work he did on one particular gas, oxygen. For he found, to everybody's surprise, that oxygen (like iron) was powerfully paramagnetic, and Michael's vivid imagination immediately carried him from the tiny soap-bubbles filled with oxygen first used to demonstrate this fact—he always loved 'playing' with soap-bubbles—to a consideration of the great question of terrestrial magnetism. Tyndall states: 'The rapidity with which these ever-augmenting thoughts assumed the form of experiments is unparalleled.'

In August 1850 Michael informed the Royal Society:

'It is hardly necessary for me to say that this Oxygen cannot exist in the atmosphere, exerting such a remarkable and high amount of magnetic force, without having a most important influence on the disposition of the magnetism of the earth as a planet, especially if it be remembered that its magnetic condition is greatly altered by variations in its density and by variations in its temperature. I think I see here the real cause of many of the variations of that force, which have been, and are now, so carefully watched on different parts of the surface of the globe. The daily variation and the annual variation both seem likely to come under it; also very many of the irregular continual variations which the photographic process of record renders so beautifully manifest. If such expectations be confirmed, and the influence of the atmosphere be found able to produce results like these, then we shall probably find a new relation between the aurora borealis and the magnetism of the earth, namely, a relation established, more or less, through the air itself in connexion with the space above it; and even magnetic relations and variations which are not as yet suspected, may be suggested and rendered manifest and measurable, in the further development of what I will venture to call *Atmospheric Magnetism*. I may be over-sanguine in these expectations, but as yet I am sustained in them by the apparent reality, simplicity and sufficiency of the cause assumed, as it at present appears to my mind. As soon as I have sufficiently submitted these views to a close consideration and the test of accordance with observation, and where applicable with experiments also, I will do myself the honour to bring them before the Royal Society.'

Within three months he fulfilled his promise by presenting two elaborate memoirs on 'Atmospheric Magnetism'. To a friend he wrote from Upper Norwood that autumn: 'We have taken a little house here on the hill-top, where I have a small room to myself, and have, ever since we came here, been deeply immersed in magnetic cogitations. I write, and write, and write. After writing, I walk out in the evening, hand-in-hand with my dear wife, to enjoy the sunset. A glorious sunset brings with it a thousand thoughts that delight me.' His experiments and his cogitations fill more than 120 printed pages; I shall give just a few sentences from Tyndall's summary of them. 'By the convergence and divergence of the lines of terrestrial magnetic force, he shows how the distribution of magnetism, in the earth's atmosphere, is affected. He applies his results to the explanation of the Annual and of the Diurnal Variation: he also considers irregular variations, including the action of magnetic storms. He discusses, at length, the observations at St. Petersburg, Greenwich, Hobarton, St. Helena, Toronto, and the Cape of Good Hope; believing that the facts, revealed by his experiments furnish the key to the variations observed at all these places.'

Tyndall adds that, the following year, he met the great Humboldt in Berlin, and his parting words were: 'Tell Faraday that I entirely agree with him. He has, in my opinion, completely explained the variation of the declination.' Humboldt was over-hasty, since this is practically the only one of Michael's researches that has not stood the test of time. There are so many factors involved—solar eruptions, cosmic rays, the Heaviside layer, etc.—then quite unknown and unsuspected. It was a wonderful piece of work all the same.

Appropriately enough, Michael returned in his last series of researches on electricity and magnetism to the topic with which he had opened the first series in 1831, the induction of electric currents by the relative motion of magnets and conducting wires. From the very start, he had visualized this induction as due to the cutting of the lines of force spreading out from the magnetic poles, lines of force depicted by the linear arrangement of iron filings scattered between these poles. He had used this idea of 'lines of force' extensively in all his subsequent work discussed in this chapter, and he now determined to demonstrate its utility by precise experiments. He found that the amount of electricity generated varied directly with the lines of force intersected; *distance* was perfectly immaterial so long as the *number* of lines intersected was the same. If a wire was moved in a uniform magnetic field with a uniform motion, then the current produced was proportional to the velocity of motion. I cannot develop either the ingenuity of his practical work or the cogency of his theoretical deductions in greater detail here, but I can quote expert opinion. Tyndall remarked in 1868: 'The beauty and exactitude of the results of this investigation are extraordinary. It is the Mont Blanc of Faraday's own achievements.' And Thompson declared in 1901: 'These memoirs should be read, and re-read, and read again, by every student of physics.'

It is important to note that, on final analysis, it becomes evident that it is really the relative motion (dynamic energy) of the wire and the magnet in all these experiments which is converted into electrical energy. This is recognized in our use of the word 'dynamo'. Similarly, in Michael's earlier experiments on the rotation of a wire carrying an electric current round a magnet, electrical energy is transformed into dynamic energy or motion. This again is recognized in our use of the word 'motor'. The magnetic field acts merely as a necessary auxiliary in each case.

There is *so* much that I must miss out completely: his work on catalysis and his work on colloids, for example. In both these fields Michael was an explorer who pointed the path that other men followed later and, following, became famous. His concluding contribution to the Royal Society—a Bakerian Lecture delivered on 5th February 1857—described optical investigations on very thin films of gold and on the ruby-coloured suspensions of ultra-microscopic particles of gold in various liquids.

That word 'suspensions' reminds me that I myself must conclude, or run the risk again of suspension for prolixity. One of Michael's lighter effusions, nevertheless, I *will* specify, whatever the penalty. It is a paper in the *Quarterly Journal of Science* for 1831, describing 'A Peculiar Class of Optical Deceptions'. (I had to cut the pages of a volume of Faraday's *Collected Researches*, published in 1858, to find it.) In this paper Michael examines the illusions that result when the eye is shown successive views of a moving body through the cogs of a revolving wheel. 'This research was, in effect, the starting point of a whole line of optical toys, beginning with the phenakistiscope or stroboscope, which developed through the zoetrope and praxinoscope into the kinematograph and animatograph of recent date.'

That quotation is from Thompson, who wrote when 'What the Butler Saw' was a novelty on seaside piers and the dawn had not yet come to Hollywood. To-day Michael's optical toys, like his electrical toys, have certainly answered the question : 'What's the use of a baby?' For his peculiar class of optical deceptions has now grown up to constitute the mammoth motion-picture industry, including three-dimensional films and television.

CHAPTER FOURTEEN

The Grand Old Boy

To grey-headed wisdom he united wonderful juvenility of spirit. Hilariously boyish upon occasion he could be, and those who knew him best knew he was never more at home, that he never seemed so pleased, as when making an old boy of himself, as he was wont to say, lecturing before a juvenile audience at Christmas.

British Quarterly Review

D espite his concentration on research, Michael never neglected his official lecturing duties at the Royal Institution. The lectures there—now as in Michael's time—fall into three types: the afternoon addresses, the Friday evening meetings, and the juvenile Christmas lectures.

The afternoon lectures consist of connected courses on all varieties of subjects, delivered by eminent scientific and literary men. One course is invariably given by the resident professor; Michael never missed giving his except during his nervous breakdowns. The Friday evening meetings, instituted by Michael in 1825, are unique. Here is what Thompson said of them in 1901: 'There is no scientific man of any original claim to distinction; no chemist, engineer, or electrician; no physiologist, geologist, or mineralogist, during the last fifty years, who has not been invited thus to give an account of his investigations. Occasionally a wider range is taken, and the eminent writer of books, dramatist, metaphysician, or musician has taken his place at the lecture-table. The Friday

159

night gathering is always a brilliant one.' To this may be appended a more picturesque extract from *Punch* in 1857; it occurs in a series of letters entitled *Mary Ann's Notions*, supposedly emanating from a fashionable young lady of the period: 'Do you know Dr. Faraday? Isn't he a dear? We went to the Royal Institution the other night, and Dr. Faraday gave a lecture. Prince Albert was there with his Star on, looking so grave and elegant. He listened with the utmost steadiness, and I do not believe he moved half a quarter of an inch all the time. But the lecture was lovely. It was quite a treat to look at dear Dr. Faraday's earnest face and silvery hair, not that he is an old man, far from it, and he is far more light and active than many a smoking stupid all-round collar man that I know. Here was Dr. Faraday, a really great man, diving into the wonderful secrets of nature, and explaining them in the ablest manner. Where were all the great men and statesmen, and the M.P.s and all those who pretend to lead the world? Listening to him as he unfolded these mighty things? Not they.'

Michael was not the born lecturer that Humphry Davy had been, he arrived at perfection by patient practice. His niece, Margaret Reid, recalls:

'Mr. Magrath used to come regularly to the morning lectures for the sole purpose of noting down for him any faults of delivery or defective pronunciation that could be detected. The list was always received with thanks; although his corrections were not uniformly adopted, he was encouraged to continue his remarks with perfect freedom. In early days he always lectured with a card before him with *Slow* written upon it in distinct characters. Sometimes he would overlook it and become too rapid; in this case, Anderson had orders to place the card before him. Sometimes he had the word

A CHRISTMAS LECTURE AT THE ROYAL INSTITUTION

(From a coloured lithograph of the painting by Blaikley. Courtesy of the Royal Institution)

The Grand Old Boy

Time on a card brought forward when the hour was nearly expired.

Yet in later life, Bence Jones tells us, his manner was so natural that thought of any art in his lecturing never occurred to anyone. Every detail was carefully prepared beforehand. He could demonstrate the most complicated and difficult experiments with invariable success, not only because he was unrivalled as a manipulator but because all had been rehearsed in advance. On the other hand, he did not disdain the use of simple experiments, even in his Friday lectures. Dr. Carpenter of Bristol relates:

'The first time I heard Faraday lecture at the Royal Institution, he was explaining the researches of Melloni. During the discourse he touched on refraction and polarization; and to explain refraction he showed the simple experiment of fixing some coloured wafers at the bottom of a basin, and then pouring in water so as to make them apparently rise. I wondered greatly at the introduction of so commonplace an experiment. Of course there were many other illustrations, and beautiful ones too. I went down, however, after the lecture, to the table, and among the crowd chatting there was an old gentleman who remarked, "I think the best experiment to-night was that of the wafers in the basin." '

Not only did Michael describe all his own memorable discoveries at these Friday evening meetings but he, who made no money on inventions himself, was always ready to be enthusiastic over the inventions of others. As Bence Jones states, 'his one object, and one alone, was to do the utmost that could be done for the discoverer'. Three examples—in addition to his lecture on the work of Melloni—may be mentioned out of many. Tyndall notes regarding a lecture he gave on the Ruhmkorff induction coil: 'I well remember the ecstasy and surprise of the *grand old man*, evoked by effects which we should now deem utterly insignificant.' On another occasion his friend Sir Charles Wheatstone (originator of the well-known Wheatstone bridge) got cold feet just before he was due to deliver a lecture and vanished, overcome by shyness; Michael, without any preparation, presented his address for him. His very last lecture, on 20th June 1862, was on Siemens's gas furnaces. Again I shall cite Thompson: 'He had been down at Swansea watching the furnaces in operation, and now proposed to describe their principle. It was rather a sad occasion, for it was but too evident that his powers were fast waning. Early in the evening he had the misfortune to burn the notes he had prepared, and became confused. He concluded with a touching personal explanation how with advancing years his memory had failed, and that in justice to others he felt it his duty to retire.'

Promoters of useful inventions also frequently benefited by the generous help of Faraday. I must confine myself to one instance, as related to Gladstone by the American millionaire, Cyrus Field.

'When I wished to unite the old and the new worlds by the telegraphic cable, I sought the advice of the great electrician, and Faraday told me that he doubted the possibility of getting a message across the Atlantic. I saw that this fatal objection must be settled at once, and begged Faraday to make the necessary experiments, offering to pay him properly for his services. The philosopher, however, declined all remuneration, but worked away at the question, and presently reported to me: "It can be done, but you will not get an instantaneous message." "How long will it take?" was my next inquiry. "Oh, perhaps a second." "Well, that's quick enough for me," was my conclusion; and the enterprise was proceeded with.'

Fie on your simplicity, Mr. Faraday! If your conscience

would not allow you to accept cash yourself, could you not have had the gumption to ask for a fat cheque for the Royal Institution, earmarked 'Purchase of Expensive Apparatus'? What a godsend it would have been to your researches! But no, you were just a child after all. I can prove it.

Michael's greatest joy was the third type of Royal Institution lectures, the Christmas courses 'adapted to a Juvenile Auditory' which he initiated in 1826. Nineteen times did he deliver this series himself, and when he talked to children the grand old man was actually transformed to a grand old boy. Let his niece, Margaret Reid, begin by telling us how he planned these lectures:

'After I went, in 1826, to stay at the Royal Institution, when my aunt was going out (as I was too little to be left alone), she would occasionally take me down to the laboratory, and leave me under my uncle's eye, whilst he was busy preparing his lectures. I had, of course, to sit as still as a mouse, with my needlework; but he would often stop and give me a kind word or a nod, or sometimes throw a bit of potassium into water to amuse me.

'In the earlier days of the Juvenile Lectures he used to encourage me to tell him everything that struck me, and where my difficulties lay when I did not understand him fully. In the next lecture he would enlarge on those especial points, and he would tell me my remarks had helped him to make things clear to the young ones. He never mortified me by wondering at my ignorance, never seemed to think how stupid I was. I might begin at the very beginning again and again; his patience and kindness were unfailing.'

Michael was always most particular in planning the experiments which illustrated these lectures. He never just told his listeners what *ought* to happen, he showed them that it *did* happen, however simple and familiar it might be. He once advised a young lecturer: 'If you say to your audience, "This stone will fall to the ground if I open my hand," then open your hand and let it fall. Take nothing for granted as known; inform the eye at the same time as you address the ear.'

Next let us hear from Lady Pollock regarding the lectures themselves: 'When he lectured to children he was careful to be perfectly distinct, and never allowed his ideas to outrun their intelligence. He took great delight in talking to them, and easily won their confidence. The vivacity of his manner and of his countenance, and his pleasant laugh, the frankness of his whole bearing, attracted them to him. They felt as if he belonged to them; and indeed he sometimes, in his joyous enthusiasm, appeared like an inspired child.' And from Lady Owen, reporting on a lecture in 1856: 'Faraday explained the magnet and strength of attraction. He made us all laugh heartily; and when he threw a coalscuttle full of coals, a poker, and a pair of tongs at the great magnet, and they stuck there, the theatre echoed with shouts of laughter.'

Michael himself was most impressed by the keenness of the boys and girls who attended; as soon as he finished they would rush up to his table to ask questions. 'Those who like it best come first', he noted, 'and they so crowd round the lecture table as to shut out the others.'

The plate facing page 160 shows him delivering the first of a series of lectures on *Metals* on 27th December 1855. The Prince Consort is in the centre of the front row of the audience, with his sons the Prince of Wales (afterwards King Edward VII) and Prince Alfred (later Duke of Edinburgh) on either hand. Sergeant Anderson stands behind Michael on the platform but, in spite of his military example, Michael's glance would now and then be raised, I am sure, from his royal auditors to a seat in the centre of the gallery where a

The Grand Old Boy

lone boy sat in 1812, listening to a lecture on *Metals* by Davy. *Eheu fugaces!*

When that series of lectures was concluded, the Prince of Wales wrote to Michael the following letter:

> *Windsor Castle,*
> 16*th January*, 1856.

M. Faraday, Esq.,

Dear Sir,

I am anxious to thank you for the advantage I have derived from attending your most interesting Lectures. Their subject, I know very well, is of great importance, and I hope to follow the advice you gave us of pursuing it beyond the Lecture Room, and I can assure you that I shall always cherish with great pleasure the recollection of having been assisted in my early studies in Chemistry by so distinguished a man.

> Believe me, Dear Sir, Yours truly,
> ALBERT EDWARD.

Three years later the young Prince did pursue chemistry beyond the Lecture Room, under the tuition of Professor Lyon Playfair at the University of Edinburgh.

May I be permitted to end this chapter on a personal note? In 1938 I was myself honoured by a request from Sir William Bragg, Director of the Royal Institution, to deliver the Christmas lectures for that year. I chose as the title of my series: *Young Chemists and Great Discoveries*; my first lecture dealt with Davy, my second with Faraday. You may conceive my emotion at standing on the same spot where my two heroes once stood, describing their sublime achievements, performing experiments they first performed, often employing the same apparatus they employed. But I reached my Everest near the finish of the lecture on Faraday. I proposed to close this lecture by reciting a section from Faraday's favourite series, *The Chemistry of a Candle*, which had been taken down in shorthand by a young chemist named Crookes (afterwards Sir William Crookes) on the occasion of its last delivery. I also suggested that this recital might be made more dramatic if I were allowed to dress myself as Faraday to do it.

Here a technical hitch arose. Since Wheatstone's escapade, described earlier in this chapter, every lecturer at the Royal Institution is carefully shadowed from the moment of his entrance to prevent a similar catastrophe; how could the Managers be sure that I would not attempt flight when I left the lecture-room for my make-up? And were the boys and girls just to sit twiddling their thumbs during my absence? These difficulties were finally overcome; I was kept under strict surveillance while a theatrical costumier equipped me with white wig and side-whiskers, Victorian frock-coat and stock, to resemble Faraday; meanwhile the lecture-table was rearranged with an elaborate display of lighted candles of all shapes and sizes, and pictures of Faraday were thrown on the lantern screen. The last two paragraphs of my recital are given below to illustrate Michael's unparalleled lucidity of exposition.

'I have here a large ball of cotton, which will serve as a wick. And, now that I have immersed it in spirit and applied a light to it, in what way does it differ from an ordinary candle? Why, it differs very much in one respect, that we have vivacity about it, a beauty entirely different from the light presented by a candle. You see those fine tongues of flame rising up. You have the same general disposition of the mass of flame from below upwards, but, in addition to that, you have this remarkable breaking out into tongues which you do not perceive in the case of a candle. Now, why is this? I must explain it to you, because when you understand that perfectly, you will be able to follow me better in what I have to say hereafter. I suppose some here will have made for themselves the experiment I am going to show you. Am I right in supposing that anybody here has played at snapdragon? I do not know a more beautiful illustration of the philosophy of flame, as to a certain part of its history, than the game of snapdragon. First, here is the dish; and let me say that when you play snapdragon properly you ought to have the dish well warmed; you ought also to have warm plums and warm brandy, which, however, I have not got. When you have put the spirit into the dish, you have the cup and the fuel; and will not the raisins act like the wicks? I now throw the plums into the dish, and light the spirit, and you see those beautiful tongues of flame that I refer to. You have the air creeping in over the edge of the dish forming these tongues. Why? Because through the force of the current, and the irregularity of the action of the flame, it cannot flow in one uniform stream. The air flows in so irregularly that you have, what would otherwise be a single image, broken up into a variety of forms, and each of these little tongues has an independent existence of its own. Indeed, I might say, you have here a multitude of independent candles.

'It is too bad that we have not got further than my game of snapdragon; but we must not, under any circumstances, keep you beyond your time. It will be a lesson to me in future to hold you more strictly to the philosophy of the thing than to take up your time so much with these illustrations.'

The children present participated in the proceeds of this experiment, of course, immediately it was over. And I also was gratified to receive a letter subsequently from one of my audience, a distant relation of Michael. It ended thus: 'My grandmother, one of his nieces, always told me how disappointed he was in having no children of his own and how happy he was in playing with his nephews and nieces. I have a scrap book that he found time to make and bind himself for their pleasure.'

Was I not right in choosing as the sub-title of this volume: *Man of Simplicity*? Let me close with one more example of his pawky humour. Mr. Joseph Newton, an assistant in the Royal Mint, was arranging some material on the lecture-table of the Royal Institution preparatory to a Friday Evening Lecture on precious metals, when he noticed an elderly, shabbily dressed person watching him. Thinking him to be a servitor of some kind, he got into conversation with him. 'I suppose you have been some years here?' 'Well, yes, a good many.' 'I hope they give you good wages.' 'Ah! I shouldn't mind being paid a little more.' And so on. Mr. Newton's surprise when he discovered that evening that he had been talking to the famous Faraday must have been overwhelming.

CHAPTER FIFTEEN

Beliefs and Disbeliefs

When Faraday opened the door of his oratory, he closed that of
his laboratory.

TYNDALL

There is no philosophy in my religion. I do not think it at all
necessary to tie the natural sources of religion together, and in
my intercourse with my fellow creatures that which is religious
and that which is philosophical have ever been two distinct things.

Letter from Faraday to
Lady Lovelace (1844)

Although Faraday locked his religious beliefs and his
scientific views (or philosophical principles, as he
preferred to call them) rigorously apart, it is necessary to discuss the former briefly to complete our apprecia-
rion of his character.

Few people can honestly keep their convictions in two com-
partments, pure reason on one side and pure faith on the
other. Faraday was one of the favoured few. In a lecture *On
Mental Education* which he delivered at the Royal Institution
on 6th May 1854, the Prince Consort being present, he said:

'Let no one suppose for an instant that the self-education I
am about to commend, in respect of the things of this life,
extends to any considerations of the hope set before us, as if
man by reasoning could find out God. It would be improper
here to enter upon this subject further than to claim an abso-

169

lute distinction between religious and ordinary belief. I shall be reproached with the weakness of refusing to apply those mental operations which I think good in high things to the very highest. I am content to bear the reproach.'

From boyhood to death he belonged, as he told Lady Lovelace, to 'a very small and despised set of Christians known, if known at all, as Sandemanians'. This sect was named after Robert Sandeman, son-in-law and successor to John Glas, who was deposed by the Presbyterian Courts in 1728 because he taught that the Church should be subject to no league or covenant, but be governed only by the doctrines of Christ and His Apostles. The Bible alone contained all that was necessary for salvation. Several tiny congregations were formed in Scotland and in England, how tiny can be seen from the statement by Frank Barnard, shortly after Faraday's death, that the London membership did not exceed twenty families, mostly quite poor. They had neither ordained ministers nor paid preachers, they made no missionary attempts to extend their numbers, no differences of opinion were tolerated.

There were three stages in their spiritual organization. The first stage was attendance at church, the second public confession of sin and profession of faith, the third election to eldership. Again, however, no effort was exerted to induce members to progress from one stage to another, the decision to go forward must be purely personal. Faraday's mother never passed beyond the first stage; Faraday himself was thirty when he did so. Yet as a small boy he hurried to complete his Sunday newspaper deliveries so as to be in time to accompany his parents to worship, and during his continental tour he complained to Abbott that travelling was almost inconsistent with religion. He made his formal profession of faith one month after his marriage, without any consultation with his wife, who was also a member of the congregation. When she asked him why he had not informed her in advance he replied: 'That is between me and my God.' Tyndall states: 'Never once, during an intimacy of fifteen years, did he mention religion to me, save when I drew him on to the subject.'

In 1840 he was elected an elder, and now it was incumbent upon him to assist at the service every Sunday, and to preach on alternate Sundays. His sermons have been described—and correctly described, to judge from samples given by Bence Jones—as a patchwork of texts cited from the Old and New Testaments. The devout earnestness of their delivery was a complete contrast to the vivacity of his manner in the lecture-room. Members of his congregation have testified that he was most assiduous in visiting the poorer brethren and sisters at their own homes, comforting them in their sorrows and afflictions, and assisting them from his own purse. Indeed, they said, he was continually pressed to be the guest of the high and noble, but he would, if possible, decline, preferring to visit some poor sister in trouble, assist her, take a cup of tea with her, read the Bible and pray. Though so full of religion, he was never obtrusive with it; it was too sacred a thing.

He held the position of elder, however, only for three years and a half. Trouble struck him in a most extraordinary way, as Thompson relates. 'One Sunday he was absent from church. When it was discovered that his absence was due to his having been "commanded" to dine with the Queen at Windsor, and that so far from expressing penitence, he was prepared to defend his action, his office became vacant. He was even cut off from ordinary membership. Nevertheless, he continued for years to attend meetings just as before. He would even return from the provincial meetings of the British Association to London for the Sunday, so as not to be absent. In 1860 he was received back as an elder, which office he held again for about three years and a half, and finally resigned it in 1864.'

Gladstone recalls: 'Among the latest of his sermons was one that he preached at Dundee about four years before his death.[1] He began by telling his audience that his memory was failing, and he feared he could not quote Scripture with perfect accuracy; and then, as said one of the elders present, "his face shone like the face of an angel," as he poured forth the words of loving exhortation.'

In 1906, a memorial tablet to Faraday was unveiled in the little chapel in London which Faraday attended. It had been converted—the Sandemanian sect having then practically died out—into a switchroom of the National Telephone Company, whose staff had originated and subscribed for the memorial. Part of Lord Kelvin's stirring speech at the ceremony follows:

'In the building in which this tablet is placed we may well repeat the celebrated Latin words—*si monumentum requiris, circumspice*—which are inscribed in St. Paul's Cathedral over the tomb of Sir Christopher Wren. Look around. These walls tell a story, not of a magnificent cathedral, but of the humble meeting-house of earnest Christian men. Here were carried on the religious services of the Sandemanians in London, a very simple association devoted to faithful and earnest Christian work. Throughout his life Faraday adhered faithfully to this denomination. I well remember, at meetings of the British Association in Aberdeen and Glasgow, how he

[1] A copy of this sermon—its actual date of delivery was 9th August 1863—has recently been discovered in the Library of University College, Dundee. According to Dr. James Riley, it is a simple homily compounded of Biblical texts and all the more impressive for its lack of adornment.

sought out the meetings of his denomination, and spent, as a preacher or worshipper there, the Sunday and any time he could spare from the work of the Association. How very interesting it is to think of Faraday's life-long faithfulness to his religious denomination. In another sense it is of very great interest to us to look around in this place and see the busy telephone operators doing their daily work in it. This also is a splendid monument to Faraday. Every electrician present, and all who are engaged in the telephonic business, will heartily agree with me in admiring and wondering at this beautiful and useful result of the vast discoveries in electromagnetism in which Faraday led the way. How much Faraday would have been delighted with the telephone some of us can imagine.'

I wonder if Faraday believed in fairies! Probably not, although, if he really had Irish blood in him, he might have allowed the existence of leprechauns. Even if good fairies did cluster around the infant Michael's cradle, bringing him gifts as desirable, though not so varied, as those for Davy, another visitor was also in evidence—the Demon King. Every time that Michael's labours led him to great achievement or high honour, something seemed bound to happen that would mar his happiness. His first discoveries in electromagnetism were followed by the accusation that he had purloined Wollaston's property; his liquefaction of chlorine was confiscated from him by Davy; his election to the Fellowship of the Royal Society involved more bitterness between him and his master; his invitation to dine with Queen Victoria resulted in his expulsion from eldership in his Church. Even the felicity of his early continental tour was blemished by petty disagreements with Lady Davy. The Demon King certainly dogged Michael's footsteps all through his career.

Beliefs and Disbeliefs

Perhaps it was Michael's own fault, for nothing pleased him more than the flashes and bangs that herald the Demon King's appearance at the pantomime. When his friend Plücker of Bonn visited London and showed him the action of a magnet upon the luminous electric discharge in vacuum tubes, it is reported that Michael got so excited that he danced around the apparatus and cried: 'Oh, to live always in it!' He gloried in thunder-storms, and would stand for hours at the window watching them, but still more he liked to be right out in them. We have already seen him running along the shore at Genoa in pelting rain during his continental tour (page 52). A friend met him once at Eastbourne in the middle of a terrific tempest, rubbing his hands with delight because he had been lucky enough to see the lightning strike a church tower. In London, if a storm wandered away in another direction, he would call a cab and chase it. Even his scientific papers bear witness to his weakness, for example: 'The chemical action of a grain of water upon four grains of zinc can evolve electricity equal in quantity to that of a powerful thunder-storm. Is there not, then, great reason to hope and believe that we shall be able to invent new instruments which shall a thousandfold surpass in energy those which we at present possess?'

It almost looks as if Michael would not be very much surprised at the atomic bomb, especially when we recall his later ideas on the ultimate particles of matter (page 154). What a pity it is that, while foreknowing the twentieth-century flaws in the atomic theory, he failed to recognize its nineteenth-century excellence! He could see the mote in Dalton's eye, but not the beam in his own.

Let us turn our attention now to one of his definite disbeliefs—table-turning. This enjoyed a tremendous vogue in

1853 and, since it was surmised that the strange force animating the furniture might be electrical in its nature, Michael was called upon to investigate it. This he did most methodically, as reported in long letters to *The Times* on June 30th and to the *Athenaeum* on July 2nd, and came to the conclusion that the true cause, except in instances of deliberate fraud, was unconscious muscular action on the part of the experimenters. He devised an ingenious apparatus to prove this, and placed it on public view in Regent Street. The general principle of this apparatus will be evident from his own description:

'A bundle of plates, consisting of sand-paper, millboard, glue, glass, plastic clay, tinfoil, cardboard, gutta-percha, vulcanized caoutchouc, wood, and resinous cement, was made up and tied together, and being placed on a table, under the hand of a turner, did not prevent the transmission of the power; the table turned or moved exactly as if the bundle had been away, to the full satisfaction of all present. The experiment was repeated, with various substances and persons, and at various times, with constant success; and henceforth no objection could be taken to the use of these substances in the construction of apparatus. The next point was to determine the place and source of motion, i.e. whether the table moved the hand, or the hand moved the table; and for this purpose indicators were constructed. One of these consisted of a light lever, having its fulcrum on the table, its short arm attached to a pin fixed on a cardboard, which could slip on the surface of the table, and its long arm projecting as an index of motion. It is evident that if the experimenter willed the table to move towards the left, and it did so move before the hands, placed at the time on the cardboard, then the index would move to the left also, the fulcrum going with the table. If the hands involuntarily moved towards the left without the table, the index would go towards the right;

and, if neither table nor hands moved, the index would itself remain immovable. The result was, that when the parties saw the index it remained very steady; when it was hidden from them, or they looked away from it, it wavered about, though they believed that they always pressed directly downwards; and, when the table did not move, there was still a resultant of hand force in the direction in which it was wished the table should move, which, however, was exercised quite unwittingly by the party operating. This resultant it is which, in the course of the waiting time, while the fingers and hands become stiff, numb, and insensible by continued pressure, grows up to an amount sufficient to move the table or the substances pressed upon. But the most valuable effect of this test-apparatus [which was afterwards made more perfect and independent of the table] is the corrective power it possesses over the mind of the table-turner. As soon as the index is placed before the most earnest, and they perceive—as in my presence they have always done—that it tells truly whether they are pressing downwards only or obliquely, then all effects of table-turning cease, even though the parties persevere, earnestly desiring motion, till they become weary and worn out. No prompting or checking of the hands is needed—the power is gone; and this only because the parties are made conscious of what they are really doing mechanically, and so are unable unwittingly to deceive themselves.'

To this description Michael added: 'I have been happy thus far in meeting with the most honourable and candid though most sanguine persons, and I believe the mental check which I propose will be available in the hands of all who desire truly to investigate the philosophy of the subject, and, being content to resign expectation, wish only to be led by the facts and the truth of nature.' Unfortunately he found that the general run of professional mediums and their disciples did not fit into this category, for a few weeks later to his old friend Schönbein he wrote: 'I have not been at work except in turning the tables upon the table-turners, nor should I have done that, but that so many inquiries poured in upon me, that I thought it better to stop the inpouring flood by letting all know at once what my views and thoughts were. What a weak, credulous, incredulous, unbelieving, superstitious, bold, frightened, what a ridiculous world ours is, as far as concerns the mind of man. How full of inconsistencies, contradictions, and absurdities it is. I declare that, taking the average of many minds that have recently come before me, and accepting for a moment that average as a standard, I should far prefer the obedience, affections, and instinct of a dog before it.'

Once more, of course, he was stepping directly into trouble. Henceforth the spiritualists, some of them people in high position, would never leave him in peace. He was reviled in the press and taunted by Mrs. Browning as a shallow materialist. He was deluged with invitations daring him to attend séances. Robert Browning, who did not share his wife's delusions, was presumably amused when Michael declined to visit the celebrated Home—mercilessly attacked by Browning in his poem *Mr. Sludge*, '*The Medium*'—saying: 'I have lost too much time about such matters already.' By 1864 he was so irritated that he wrote to another charlatan: 'Whenever the spirits can counteract gravity or originate motion, or supply an action due to natural physical force, or counteract any such action; whenever they can punch or prick me, or affect my sense of feeling or any other sense, or in any other way act on me without my waiting on them; or working in the light can show me a hand, either writing or not, or in any way make themselves visibly manifest to me; whenever these things are done or anything which a conjuror

M   177

cannot do better; or, rising to higher proofs, whenever the spirits describe their own nature, and like honest spirits say what they can do, and so make *themselves* manifest; whenever by such-like signs they come to me, and ask my attention to them, I will give it. But until some of these things be done, I have no more time to spare for them.'

We, a century later, comparing the marvellous development of Michael's own researches with the stationary plight of the table-turners, still trying the same stale tricks, can sympathize with his asperity at the impediment they imposed upon him. But remembering the number of dupes that persists to-day, we may ask ourselves the same question that *Punch* asked in 1853: 'Do *we* of enlightenment consider this an age?'

CHAPTER SIXTEEN

The End of the Road

Sweet Thames, run softly, till I end my song.

Spenser

I t is remarkable how closely Faraday's career is connected with the river Thames. He was born in London just south of it, he grew up and he worked for more than fifty years in London just north of it, he carried out some of his most significant experiments at Woolwich a few miles downstream, and he spent his last years at Hampton Court a few miles upstream.

In 1855 he hit the headlines when he sent a letter to *The Times* calling attention to the dangerous state of the river, which he described as 'a real sewer'. Steaming up the Thames one July day in a penny boat—one of the fastest forms of transport at that time—he was appalled at its offensiveness. Wetting some white cards to make them sink easily, he dropped pieces into the river at each pier. They disappeared from sight at once in the 'opaque pale brown fluid', although the sun was shining brightly, proof enough of the impurity of the water. Shortly afterwards *Punch* issued the cartoon reproduced on page 180, and noted that if matters were remedied more lives might be saved than by Humphry Davy's safety-lamp.

Although he made a good recovery from his first nervous breakdown and did much excellent work afterwards,

Faraday giving his Card to Father Thames

(Courtesy of the Managers of *Punch*)

The End of the Road

Michael's strength was steadily failing, and he found it necessary to take frequent holidays to recuperate, some affording him the pleasure of renewing contact with old friends on the Continent. In 1858 Queen Victoria, at the suggestion of the Prince Consort, offered him the life use of a house on Hampton Court Green. It required extensive repair, and poor Michael—literally still *poor* Michael—doubted whether he could pay the necessary expenses. When a hint of this reached the Queen, she directed at once that it should be put into perfect condition, both inside and out, before he and Sarah took up residence. They still kept their rooms at the Royal Institution, however, and Michael continued to experiment and lecture there, while it was in session, for several years.

In October 1861, he announced his wish to retire, but the Managers of the Royal Institution, lightening his duties, refused to accept his resignation. It was not until March 1865, after several more courteous rebuffs, that he gave up his position of superintendent of the house and laboratories of the Royal Institution, with which he had been connected for well over fifty years. In May 1865, he sent his last report to the Trinity House; it was on St. Bees lighthouse in Cumberland. His work on the use of the magneto-electric spark in lighthouse illumination had taken him to all parts of England, and had saved the lives of many seamen; he handed it over to Tyndall. It was with the greatest difficulty that he was persuaded to agree to the decision of the Corporation that his salary of £200 per annum should continue as long as he lived. His aversion to receiving 'something for nothing' remained just as strong as in Melbourne's day (page 127).

So he sat quietly in his room at Hampton Court, or took short walks along the Thames and in Bushy Park, nursing his memories. To a friend who asked him how he was, he replied simply: 'Just waiting'. His several nieces, now mature women, cheerfully took turns in mothering him and Sarah; one of them wrote in 1867: 'I spent June at Hampton Court. Dear uncle kept up rather better; still the sweet unselfish disposition was there, winning the love of all around him. I shall never look at the lightning flashes without recalling his delight in a beautiful storm. I shall also always connect the sight of the hues of a brilliant sunset with him, and especially he will be present to my mind while I watch the fading of the tints into the sombre gray of night. He loved to have us with him, as he stood or sauntered on some open spot, and spoke his thoughts perhaps in the words of Gray's Elegy, which he retained in memory clearly long after many other things had faded quite away. Then, as darkness stole on, his companions would gradually turn indoors, while he was well pleased to be left to solitary communing with his own thoughts.'

What were those thoughts? They covered so many topics, so many people. Thoughts of his father's smithy; Gladstone tells us: 'When he was sitting to Noble for his bust, it happened one day that the sculptor, in giving the finishing touches to the marble, made a clattering with his chisels: noticing that his sitter appeared *distrait*, he said that he feared the jingling of the tools had annoyed him, and that he was weary. "No, my dear Mr. Noble," said Faraday, putting his hand on his shoulder, "but the noise reminded me of my father's anvil, and took me back to my boyhood." '

Thoughts of his schooldays, revived by the evidence that he had been called upon to give before the Public Schools Commission in 1862. 'I am not an educated man,' he said, 'I know very little of the Public Schools.' He complained that the teaching of science was almost completely overlooked by them: 'the highly educated man fails to understand the simplest things of science.' Asked at what age science teaching might begin at school, he cited his Christmas Lectures and hesitated to give a lower limit. 'I never yet found a boy who was not able to understand by simple explanation, and to enjoy the point of an experiment. I do think that the study of natural science is so glorious a school for the mind, that with the laws impressed on all these things by the Creator, and the wonderful unity and stability of matter, and the forces of matter, there cannot be a better.'

Many thoughts of Humphry Davy as he first knew him— later guilt was all forgotten, only the morning glory remained. Improvident Michael, with his infinite trust in Providence, subscribed most liberally to the fund for raising a monument to Humphry at Penzance. Thoughts also of Lady Davy, recently dead in Rome. Thoughts of that Grand Tour of Europe. How he had seen Napoleon I driving in state in Paris; Napoleon III was now Emperor there, he had corresponded with Michael on scientific matters prodigiously when he was a wretched prisoner in the Fortress of Ham in 1843, he had made him a Commander of the Legion of Honour in 1856, his star also was soon doomed to fall. How Humphry and he had driven through the fairy forest of Fontainebleau—the chestnut avenue in Bushy Park, which he adored, would remind him of that—how they had climbed Vesuvius. How he had worn that old nightcap when crossing the Alps and taking part in the Carnival revels.

And those revels would remind him, as he sat watching the waters of the Thames, so clear at Hampton, of the many happy picnics he had taken with Sarah and with groups of congenial friends on the river in the early years of their married life, picnics followed by choruses and charades during the homeward journey. Michael sang bass in these choruses, and unlike Humphry sang correctly both as to time and tune; he also played on the flute, but only in his bachelor days. Sarah's indulgence *did* have its limits.

Thoughts of his old comrades, Abbott and Phillips in England, De La Rive and Schönbein on the Continent, others on both sides of the Channel too numerous to mention. Thoughts of Schönbein's daughter Emilie, who had lived in London and endeared herself to Michael and Sarah; they grieved over her sudden death in 1859 as deeply as if she had been their own child. Thoughts of his nephews and nieces, who still comforted him in his childlessness. Birds singing in the branches would awaken recollections of how he used to take them, many times a day on country vacations, to watch a blackbird in a cherry-tree feeding its young. Sheep grazing on the green would bring memories of how interested they (and he) were in watching lambs trying vainly to find their mothers after shearing-time.

Thoughts of the table-turners, who still pestered him? No, other thoughts were more pressing.

Thoughts, above all, of his beloved Sarah. Here I must draw upon Lady Pollock's reminiscences: 'Sometimes he was depressed by the idea of his wife left without kin—of the partner of his hopes and cares deprived of him. She had been the first love of his ardent soul; she was the last; she had been the brightest dream of his youth, and she was the dearest comfort of his age; he never ceased for an instant to feel himself happy with her; and he never for one hour ceased to care for her happiness. It was no wonder, then, that he felt anxiety about her. But he would rally from such a trouble with his great religious trust, and looking at her with moist eyes, he would say, "I must not be afraid; you will be cared for, my wife; you will be cared for." There are some who remember how tenderly he used to lead her to her seat at the Royal Institution when she was suffering from lameness;

The End of the Road

how carefully he used to support her; how watchfully he used to attend all her steps. It did the heart good to see his devotion, and to think what the man was and what he had been.'

Just waiting. Gradually his memories became more and more blurred, he passed away, sitting peacefully in his chair in his study, on 25th August 1867. By his own desire his funeral, conducted in silence, was strictly plain and private. There were those, his niece Jane Barnard notes, who would have liked it otherwise, but Michael's last wishes were respected. He has no tomb in Westminster Abbey, his simple grave in Highgate Cemetery looks out over the London he loved so well, the London where he laboured so long.

The deep distinction between the characters of Davy and Faraday has been dwelt upon in my previous book *Humphry Davy: 'Pilot' of Penzance*. To the several pairs of analogous celebrities there cited I shall add just one more here—Browning and Tennyson. Browning had all the complexity and combativeness of Davy; Tennyson all the simplicity and serenity of Faraday. The last verses of each poet are typical.

Browning's *Epilogue* might have been expressly written for Humphry's brother John, called to his bedside in the middle of the night at Geneva when a third paralytic stroke killed him:

At the midnight in the silence of the sleep-time,
When you set your fancies free,
Will they pass to where—by death, fools think, imprisoned—
Low he lies who once so loved you, whom you loved so,
Pity me?

For John would have answered triumphantly:

The End of the Road

No, at noonday in the bustle of man's work-time
*   Greet the unseen with a cheer!*
Bid him forward, breast and back as either should be,
"Strive and thrive," cry "Speed,—fight on, fight ever
*   There as here!"*

Michael's tranquil leave-taking of life, on the other hand, is precisely depicted in Tennyson's *Crossing the Bar*:

> *Sunset and evening star,*
> *   And one clear call for me!*
> *And may there be no moaning of the bar,*
> *   When I put out to sea.*

Since Michael himself would have re-echoed the ending of the poem:

> *For tho' from out our bourne of Time and Place*
> *   The flood may bear me far,*
> *I hope to see my Pilot face to face*
> *   When I have crost the bar.*

And Michael's simple faith would, I am confident, add to that meeting with his Heavenly Pilot a reunion with his earthly pilot—the Pilot of Penzance—at whose feet he could again sit in perfect amity.

Before I conclude, I am compelled to add a few words on that eternal controversy: 'Who was the greater scientist, Davy or Faraday?' There is no argument as to who was the greater *man*, and I suspect that an overwhelming majority of those who have read both my books, although I have done my utmost to maintain impartiality, will record their vote for Faraday as the greater scientist also. Nevertheless, I myself

The End of the Road

still hesitate to give my personal preference. The point that I can never forget is this—*without Davy there would have been no Faraday*.

Davy had a single splendid opportunity to enlist a successor, and grasped that opportunity. Faraday, however, wrote: 'I have often endeavoured to discover a genius, but have not been very successful, though many cases seemed promising at first.' More than one biographer has doubted whether Michael actually did try hard enough, whether he might not have doubled his achievements by associating with himself Clerk Maxwell (page 138), for example. It is uncertain that he ever had a real chance to capture Clerk Maxwell—'Daftie Maxwell' his schoolmates at the Edinburgh Academy called him when he presented a paper to the Royal Society of Edinburgh at the age of thirteen—although they were in very close touch for a time. Lady Lovelace, a woman of the highest talent, proposed in 1844 'to become his disciple and to go through with him all his own experiments'; his reasoned refusal—too long to repeat here—must have puzzled and disappointed her sorely. Crookes (page 166), to whom he gave the advice: 'Work, finish, publish,' might possibly have collaborated with him later, but Crookes was a spiritualist. A student at King's College wrote to Michael in 1834, asking his comments on some atomic speculations; Michael replied politely: 'I can say nothing about them. The more I think the less distinct does my idea of an atom become.' He advised his young correspondent to experiment: 'Whether you confirm or confute your views, good must come from your exertions' —but made no attempt to meet him. How differently Davy acted in 1812! No, Michael was essentially a solitary worker, nothing would satisfy him but perfection. His own confession is illuminating: 'I never could work, as some Professors do most extensively, by students or pupils. All the work had to be my own.' Surely Michael's sin of omission in failing to find a follower counterbalances to some extent Humphry's more obvious sins of commission!

As Gladstone admits, Michael himself was no 'model of all the virtues', dreadfully uninteresting and discouraging to the ordinary mortal. His inner life was a battle, with its wounds as well as its victories. Lord Cardwell was witness to a crushing reproof he once administered to a barrister who attempted to bully him in court. His constant disparagement of Sturgeon (page 114), to whom he should surely have been sympathetic, is a strange exception to his normal kindliness. He was more disposed to turn away in disgust from an erring companion than to endeavour to reclaim him, and the rigidity of his religious views hampered his sociability in many circles. Nevertheless, Tyndall assures us: 'There was no trace of asceticism in his nature. He preferred the meat and wine of life to its locusts and wild honey.' He enjoyed attending Royal Academy dinners; Turner and Landseer were his close friends; Turner's sunsets and storms had a particular appeal to him. He occasionally went to the opera and to the theatre, sitting in the cheaper seats, but he liked slipping away from London with Sarah on little sketching excursions still more.

Dumas stated in his eulogy before the French Academy of Sciences: 'There was nothing dramatic in the life of Faraday. It should be presented under that simplicity of aspect which is the grandeur of it.' I cannot agree with the first sentence, although I trust I have satisfied the sentiment of the second. I find plenty of drama in the life of Faraday, but no trace of the melodrama that filled the life of Davy. From the rise to the fall of the curtain, Michael was in quest of the Holy Grail; Tyndall rightly terms him: 'Just and faithful knight of God.'

The End of the Road

The following verses are part of a long anonymous poem that appeared in *Punch* a month after Michael's death:

One rule his life was fashioned to fulfil:
  That he who tends Truth's shrine, and does the hest
Of Science, with a humble, faithful will,
  The God of Truth and Knowledge serveth best.

And from his humbleness what heights he won!
  By slow march of induction, pace on pace,
Scaling the peaks that seemed to strike the sun,
  Whence few can look, unblinded, in his face.

Yet, living face to face with these great laws,
  Great truths, great myst'ries, all who saw him near
Knew him for child-like, simple, free from flaws
  Of temper, full of love that casts out fear:

Untired in charity, of cheer serene;
  Not caring world's wealth or good word to earn;
Childhood's or manhood's ear content to win;
  And still as glad to teach as meek to learn.

Did ever any other British scientist deserve such a popular tribute? Yet, deeply as Michael was mourned in Britain, Dumas was right when he said in the First Faraday Lecture of the Chemical Society in London in 1869: 'The name of your illustrious fellow countryman is not one which can be claimed by any single nation as its exclusive property.' I myself, who taught for fifteen years in America, have testified: 'Faraday would have made a wonderful American, his nature was probably nearer to Abraham Lincoln's than to that of any other person of his period.' Let Dumas, however, continue, since later Faraday Lecturers from Italy, Germany,

The End of the Road

Russia, the United States and Sweden have all endorsed his statement: 'Faraday belongs to the whole world.' And so let Shakespeare furnish for him a fitting epitaph:

> *His life was gentle, and the elements*
> *So mix'd in him that Nature might stand up*
> *And say to all the world "This was a man!"*

Index

193

Index

194

Index

195

Index